YOU AND I:

A WORK
IN PROGRESS

BY

JOHN HINSEY

Manuscript preparation provided by
UBIQUITY PRODUCTIONS

This book is dedicated to the volunteers of the Adult Center of Prescott, Inc. as well as to those volunteers the world over who generously provide services that are so beneficial to others.

In recognition of its exemplary service to the Prescott community, all income realized through the Adult Center's promotion and sale of this written work is to be the exclusive property of the Adult Center.

John Hinsey

ISBN catalogue number pending.

Published by:
The Adult Center of Prescott, Inc.
335 East Aubrey Street
Prescott, Arizona 86303

CHAPTER 1

My wife, Sue, is a very good bridge player. Because she has such a keen interest in the game, I gained a new, amicable, and as it turned out, a very wise friend. This friend enabled me see the world and its people more clearly and distinctly than ever before.

Before trying to write an account of his views, I looked up "insight" in a thesaurus. Insight was what I had acquired. I wanted to find something expressive, something that gives the word real importance. I found under a reference to "Understanding Others" the following: "Until we know what motivates the hearts and minds of men we can understand nothing outside ourselves, nor will we ever reach fulfillment as the greatest miracle of all, the human being," Mary Mannes, More in Anger, (1958).

That quote helped bring together all of what he had revealed to me. Hopefully, it will help you accept what this exceptional person believed so unconditionally.

First, I would like to tell you how we met.

Four years ago, with Social Security checks assured, Sue and I retreated from Southern California, that unpredictable place that was once so enjoyable, to Prescott, Arizona. After numerous

1

stays in this handsome, most gracious city, we finally bought a house and made the move. The last move we'll ever make, if we comply with Sue's wishes...

It took us a while to get fully settled. There was the usual painting to be done to our taste and draperies to be decided upon. In the main, however, we had to get used to being together all day long. I, also, had to become accustomed to life without the normal pressures of maintaining a small real estate brokerage in Laguna Beach. Surprisingly, I adapted in short order. Lunch together at the "Grill" or "Murphy's" or the Hassayampa Hotel became quiet celebrations. While having a cocktail and appreciating the good food, I learned not to look at my watch. And the undisciplined afternoons brought about naps that proved to be unplanned, romantic adventures.

When I talked to old friends back in California, they inevitably asked, "How's retirement?" I would, following just a few weeks of this release from mortgage fluctuations and schedules, nonchalantly reply, "I was born for it." And I was and I still am!

It was about three months later, that Sue said one morning over coffee, "I think I'll go to the Adult Center after lunch. There's a sanctioned duplicate game there every Tuesday." She looked over to me for my reaction.

I had wondered how long the allure or the

challenge of the cards could be held off. She didn't bother to ask if I'd go with her. She knew that we didn't share an interest or commitment to the science of duplicate bridge.

"Do you have a partner?"

"Usually there's someone available. If not, at least I'll get acquainted. What will you do?"

"Oh, I've got the garden to cope with. Don't worry, there's plenty to do. I'll keep busy."

We had an early lunch and she left a little after twelve.

I had just turned on CNN's half hour of news at 4:30 when I heard the garage door open and the car pull in. She walked through the door with a bright smile that told me that things had gone well.

"Hi, how was your day?"

I answered, "Fine! Yours?"

She said, "You know how we've always felt that good fortune often follows a chance happenstance." I nodded. She went on, "Well, I talked to the director, her name is Gwen Thomas, a delightful lady, and she introduced me to a woman who was also there for the first time. Her name is Bobbie Andrews. Bobbie's from the San Francisco area and she and her husband moved here about the same time we did. He, too, by the way, is not a bridge player."

I smiled my approval saying, "You're sounding as if you got along. I mean as far as your game was concerned."

"We did. Exceptionally. It was as if I was playing with Nina back in Laguna. I think we did well. There were a few mistakes, but that's to be expected."

"Are you going to play together again?"

"We made a date for next Tuesday." She glanced at me, "Unless, of course, something comes up." I said nothing. "I have her number and she has mine. So we'll see. I hope we can, I liked her very much." There was a pause before, "I know you will, too."

Later there was a call from Gwen. They had placed second out of eleven tables. Sue was really pleased. She called Bobbie and I could tell from her end of the conversation that a partnership had been newly formed.

I met Bobbie and her husband, Quinn, perhaps a month later. We were invited to dinner and some casual and surely some inexact bridge later.

Bobbie was what I expected from Sue's description. She was short, delightfully chubby, with a lingering smile that spread quickly to one that was warm, and instantly captivating. Matching the smile was a whirlwind and spontaneous wit. She was loaded with good cheer, a kick to be around.

Quinn was the opposite. Tall, slim, with a craggy, close-to-splendid head and face. He looked Lincolnesque to me, sans beard. In repose, he appeared solemn, but when he smiled, his eyes would light up and there was this startling transformation. I liked him. We chatted easily while sipping

4

our wine, awaiting dinner. After dinner the four of us talked until near midnight. Bridge was forgotten, to my relief—and I assume, Quinn's.

The evening went beyond my expectations. As we were leaving, Quinn suggested that we have lunch at the "Grill" the next time Bobbie and Sue played at the Adult Center. I readily agreed.

It was this suggestion that was the beginning of a fortunate arrangement—due to happenstance—that lasted for over three years. Whenever our wives played cards, which grew to more than once a week, we met. At first, it was in our favorite restaurant. But as time passed, we often convened in one of our homes. As much fun as it was at the Grill's bar, frequently our conversations demanded less conviviality. We found it was more comfortable at home.

Our discussions encompassed the whole of life. We talked politics, religions, those great taboos. We reviewed the good and bad movies we'd seen. All of the latest fiction and nonfiction books that one of us deemed worthwhile, were exchanged. Literally, we talked about everything, drawing from lots of stored up experiences as they related to the eddy of current events.

I had long held the view that to be successful in real estate, you had to listen carefully to your client. If you want to convince someone, you've got to be open to conviction yourself. In other words, be attentive to what is being said. It is clear to me today that that is what governed all of our discussions. Each of us listened to the other. No matter what we said to make a point, or how ridiculous the point may have been to begin with, not once did either of us fail to listen with genuine consideration.

There was reciprocal civility, the like of which I had seldom known. We were never competitive with one another. If we disagreed, it was only after careful deliberation. Then, we would make our own view known separate from the slightest hint of mockery or derision. There was no attempt at one-upmanship. This gave us the freedom to say those things that might not normally be said. Without misgivings, very private opinions and sentiments were freely placed at the other's disposal.

One afternoon, I don't remember just when it was, he asked me, "How would you describe this world without us?"

I couldn't help but laugh. I said, "Without you and me? I think the world would be precisely as it is and would continue to be whatever it is going to be. No difference."

He smiled and said, "My fault. I meant what would our planet Earth be like minus the human race?"

Well, that was the origin of weeks of discussions. Every time we got together, we progressed along a line wholly controlled by Quinn.

I'm sorry to say that my good friend is gone

now. I miss him terribly. He left a big hole that will probably never be filled. He died in his favorite chair, reading. Suddenly and inexplicably his heart stopped. No history of heart trouble. When Bobbie called, it was incomprehensible that we would not meet the next Tuesday. Even more inconceivable was the reality that we would never meet again. Bobbie was devastated, almost beyond help. For weeks she was certainly beyond banal reason.

CHAPTER 2

There is no growth except in the
fulfillment of obligations.

Saint-Exupery

It was six months after his death before Bobbie tried playing bridge again.

On the day she came by to pick up Sue, she brought with her a fairly thick manila envelope. Bobbie said to me, "I've finally gotten to the point that I can go through Quinn's things. I found this in the top drawer of his desk." She handed it to me.

I said, "What is it?"

"I know about the last conversations you and Quinn had. He told me a little about them and how much he enjoyed your times together." She tried to smile, but didn't quite make it. "Inside are notes. Some of them don't make a great deal of sense to me. Too cryptic. Some seem unfinished. But I'm sure you can decipher them. You're mentioned throughout. John said this, John said that—that sort of thing. I think you should have them. They'll mean more to you than to me."

When Bobbie and Sue left, I immediately bent to open the envelope's metal fastener. Inside were neatly margined and lined sheets of notebook paper filled with Quinn's handwriting. I scanned the pages and realized that he had, in chronological order, set down outlines of our discussions. If I hadn't been a participant in those discussions, his notes could, indeed, be puzzling or obscure. Or unfinished, as Bobbie said. To me those pages brought everything back. Reading a brief comment would trigger my memory. I could, with little trouble, visualize and hear him. His ideas came flooding back.

I was stunned. I never suspected that he had written anything down. Obviously, this note making followed our afternoons together. That made sense because all of his assertions were, I always felt, unrehearsed. There had to have been preplanning, but his commentary, filled as it was with pauses and reflection, was too unstudied. It was not what I would call spontaneous or thoughts off the cuff, but he did now and then give that impression.

Those dialogues that followed his question about what would the world be like minus the human race had haunted me. Nonetheless, I didn't know what to do with what was there, sometimes spinning around in my head. With these papers in hand, I knew what lay ahead. For weeks I had

9

regretted that his views were not recorded. I firmly believe his convictions, which were more humane than scholarly, should be available to whomever thinks or cares about the future, ours and our world.

So, what follows will be an attempt to recapture our hours of conversations. I start with a great desire to be accurate and thorough. I also enter upon this project filled with trepidation. Sure, I know that if I'm not up to the task, I can stop. I think knowing that takes my anxiety level even higher. I don't want to fail myself or my exceptional friend. The only way I can fail or succeed, however, is to try and fulfill this self-imposed obligation. I know of no other way to begin than going back to that unexpected question and carry on.

CHAPTER 3

*Man hath all which nature hath, but more
and in more lies all his hopes of good.*
Mathew Arnold

Again, the question was, "What would our planet be like minus the human race?" I recall that I thought for a moment and then said, "Obviously, the continents would be as they are now, as would the great bodies of water."

He interjected, "Except for the Panama and Suez Canals and those dams that have changed the courses of rivers and formed new lakes."

I acknowledged that, of course, he was right and went on, "Nature would reign uninterrupted by our sprawl, our machines and industry. Vegetation and animal life would flourish. I see the earth in terms of impenetrable forests and wide stretches of unblemished deserts and plains. The mountain ranges and canyons around the world certainly would be the same." I added in a moment, "Hurricanes, volcanic eruptions, lightening strikes and floods would leave their marks, but those scars would only alter things temporarily."

I waited, not sure how to continue.

He stepped in saying, "We still have our ecosystems, though those communities of plants and animals have been reduced or diminished by humankind's persistent invasions. These ecosystems, without us imposing on their natural aim toward balance, would, to use your term, 'flourish.' But, I believe, no one system would dominate the earth, nor would one creature dominate the systems. Only once, as far as we know, did a creature reign supreme and that was the dinosaur. During the Jurassic period, before these mighty flesh-eaters and plant-eaters mysteriously disappeared, mammals were relatively small. Archaeologists tell us that any change in these animals and their populations was negligible over millions of years. It is left to us to wonder what the world would be like if they had continued to rule and evolve. We can assume not as it was a hundred thousand years ago nor, for that matter, as it is today."

I offered, "Nature probably learned her lesson with the dinosaurs. I suppose we can also assume that the earth, free of one creature's dominance and the human influence, would be ecologically stable."

Quinn smiled and said, "I see it as a virtual paradise. All living things agreeably combined, that is, from nature's point of view. There would be an unrestrained harmony, however unfortunate that harmony might be maintained by the predators and their prey. Balance and beauty would prevail even though cries would echo the distress of all the victims in the food chain."

We sat for a while mulling this over. As I remember, he got up, went into the kitchen for another cup of coffee. He asked if I wanted more and I indicated no. On the way back he said, "What would be missing in this paradise?"

I didn't quite understand his question, so I said, "What do you mean exactly?"

"Without us what would be lacking?"

I had to learn that when he said "us," he meant the human race. My response, I thought, was hardly worthwhile, but anyway I said, "Roads, towns, cities, pollution, the geometric boundaries of farmer's crops."

"True enough, but wouldn't the whole of four and one-half billion years of the earth's progress be meaningless? What difference would it make whether the great diversity of life existed or continued? I see insignificance where there is no wonder about the world, no curiosity about the universe. How could there be relevance if there is no one to be amazed that a bulky elephant lives alongside a spindly giraffe? I feel it senseless to have all the planet's beauty endure with no intelligence to cherish it. Or absurd where there is no pity for the sick, the lame or the dying. Think about it, there wouldn't be creatures capable of self-improvement. Only the slow process of adaptation would bring about change. Imagination, spontaneous and revolutionary invention would have no

13

role. There would be no thought given to the unknowns, or the mysterious function of fate. A God's work would prevail unacknowledged. Creation itself would be unacknowledged. Simple survival would be the principle drive for all living things."

Quinn had become more impassioned than normal as he developed his theme. He settled back in his chair and finished with less intensity, "We may be destructive in fulfilling our desire for progress, but if we had not come about, this life-giving earth would be of little or no consequence. We give it meaning while it sustains us because we are aware of its splendors, its history and its secrets."

I was caught a little off guard by his depth of feeling. Unusual for him. I accepted fully what he had said so well but could only respond with, "A paradise has no meaning?"

Almost playfully, he said, "Maybe to a Supreme but selfish creator who wants for his or her pleasure a self-sustaining zoo." He went on more seriously, "But not when all the creatures in it are so rigidly controlled. Not when behavior patterns are set and impossible to be made different by those accorded the patterns. Animals are limited by their individual genetic and physical make ups. Animal choices are arranged." He stopped briefly and said, "Programmed or preset may be better characterizations. Patterns of behavior from their genetic backgrounds never deviate. They react

14

solely to their own built-in survivalist impulses and their own particular biological needs. That's it. They, of course, adapt, but they do not or cannot manipulate their environment or alter the conditions of their environment. Animals don't envision, picture in their minds things not yet in existence. Existing as they do, inherently regulated, they can inhabit a paradise without astonishment, respect or intellectual exhilaration. Why a paradise without some living thing to appreciate and venerate it?"

I had gradually become engrossed in what came close to a lecture. To keep him going, I asked, "You don't see the human being as a spoiler of this paradise?"

"Indeed, I do not."

"If not as ecological bunglers, how do you see us?"

"The only reference we have is other life here in this world. Compared with life, as we know it, I see the human race to be a magnificent, awe-inspiring, clearly unmatched collection of superb beings."

He said, "You know, John, the ultimate human mystery is the nature of our consciousness or self-awareness. With the possible exception of the great apes, animals are incapable of being conscious of their existence. We alone are endowed with a peerless intellect. We are not locked in to any one role like other creatures. Our exclusive

15

brain allows us to make choices, good ones and those that prove to be disastrous. We are limitless. We are equally free to overcome or succumb to adversity. Like every other living thing, we strive to survive, but we can sacrifice ourselves for causes that appear greater than our clinging to life. And, finally, human beings are able to fulfill their most fanciful dreams. No other creature has these remarkable as well as phenomenal capacities."

Soberly he said, "The great human tragedy is that we don't see and accept ourselves for what we are."

I said quickly, anxious for his answer, "If not accepting ourselves for what we are is a tragedy, what can we do to avoid an unhappy and disastrous ending?" I asked. "All true tragedies end badly, do they not?"

He looked away and after consideration said, "I won't go so far as to say this is the solution, but it would help just to take a closer look at ourselves."

I responded, "Let's do that then. I understand about our intellect. I know we make choices, some monumental, others trivial. What else should we see? How else should we view humanity?"

"Well," he said, taking a small sip of what must have been very cold coffee, "we are set apart from any other thing in our tiny corner of the universe. We can do as we please with whatever nature or a god's proficiency has produced over billions of years. Humankind is not required to contribute to an order which without us would have everything functioning properly and everything in its proper place. Only the human being has had the power to destroy or enhance those conditions."

"I see that. We do have that power. It's a shame we aren't more willing to enhance rather than destroy."

Quinn looked at me and said, "Some are trying to preserve. We may yet learn to enhance."

I indicated concurrence and said, "Go on."

"There is no inborn provision that we behave following those specific patterns that govern every other living thing. We can function by an unrivaled, but hardly error-free, logic. We determine objectives and we alone develop or alter them. Our human characteristics are ours alone. It's only human beings that can initiate and fine tune events to fit their own needs. We have the same freedom to decide whether to maintain, to destroy or to enhance ourselves as we have the freedom to do as we please with our supportive planet."

I recall that he warmed again to his subject and continued with his comments beginning to flow as he progressed. "I don't see an outside force ruling us absolutely."

I couldn't help but ask, "What about God?"

He shook his head, "We are neither accommodated or restricted by a supernatural being or a universal life force. Nature, obviously, does not control us."

I didn't interrupt.

"We are free to believe that Moses received a code for correct behavior from his all-merciful God. We must also acknowledge, however, that when he left that shrouded mountain it was up to him and those waiting to comply or not. We can believe that our gods set standards, but we must also accept all of the hard evidence that proves we have either chosen to live by those standards or consistently chosen to reject them."

"We are back to the freedom of choice. Do you believe that is what essentially makes us unique?"

"Partly, of course. Without our drives and desires free of constraints, though, choice wouldn't mean much would it? No different than a tiger's decision to go to the right or left when prowling. Choice is important; we are independent, inexplicably so. According to what we believe, we, by selection, manage ourselves and our destiny.

"Human beings are a species, but individually we can be incredibly different. Separate customs, traditions, a variety of myths and histories —our cultures—are responsible for those differences. Cultural isolationism has proved to be not only stubborn, but a source of willful and unreasonable pride. Some of our problems would be resolved if we learned that by addressing life differently underscores our freedom to be, do and think as we please. Our ability to originate and live by dissimilar approaches to life are signs of, really proof of, human distinction and unconditional superiority."

"We should look at differences as a plus, as an indication of mankind's superiority. That's your point?"

"Absolutely. Whatever our religion or whatever political system or set of traditions we live under, we are basically the same in our drives." He thought for a moment before saying, "These drives, I'll get to them later."

I remember that this was the first hint that we were just beginning to explore something to which he had given a great deal of thought. I said, "You're saying we're different but the same?"

"Yes. We are a species after all. Our blood and vital organs are interchangeable, when matched, of course. Like skin color and facial characteristics, languages and our backgrounds are unimportant when we take into account our invariables, our consistencies."

I did say, "You've thought this all out thoroughly, haven't you?"

"Guilty, as charged." A transformation took place that I'd mentioned. A wide smile changed his eyes. All of the gravity disappeared.

"One last point, then I'll quit for today." Almost light heartedly he said, "Our rise above nature's order is complete. It's complete except for our reliance on the air that surrounds us, and the food and water that this planet provides. Those things under nature's control accommodate us. But, again, this incredibly powerful source doesn't ask for repayment, nor does this source make decisions for us. No other living thing of which is known can make this claim."

"We are unique! What were your other terms? Magnificent was one, I remember."

"It doesn't matter. Collectively, we are without a doubt, magnificent creatures. I think I said earlier we were awe-inspiring and unmatched. All of that is true. I think it makes one feel better to believe it's true. That in itself could reduce the dire promises of my suggested tragedy."

It was about 4:00 when he left. Sue wasn't home yet. I sat and reviewed what had taken place. When Sue walked in around 4:30 and asked, "How was your day," I said simply, "Very interesting. Yes, very interesting." That was all I could say.

CHAPTER 4

Every man carries the entire
form of human condition.

Montaigue

The usual couple of days passed before we met again.

Quinn drove to our house. Sue had fixed us a delicious lunch of pasta primevera. As we ate, we talked about the latest political polls—or something equally unimportant. With the dishes in the dishwasher—and not turned on so its noisy efficiency would bother us—we got comfortable. I didn't have to prompt him. He was set to further analyze the human being.

I want to mention here that the preceding dialogues were written to the best of my recollection. His notes were invaluable, but most were incomplete with regard to his exact language. I've put words in his mouth, to be sure, and will as I recount the weeks that followed. I believe the words will be consistent with his thinking, his point of view on any given day and his attitude. With this understood, I'll continue.

He said, without preamble, "We stand apart from the other creatures here on earth. Several months ago we discussed why it is that we are so

21

distinct."

I said, "I remember. We had read about a new science ."

"Correct. According to these geneticists, something extraordinary took place in the brains of our ancestors. In primitive humans or humanoids, a minute change in neurons made their brains function differently."

I thought back to that particular afternoon and said, "Their belief is that a genetic alteration turned our late predecessors into the only living species of human. This produced a change that accounts for our ability to speak, to imagine, to evaluate and to plan ahead."

"Yes. The important thing is, though, that this change occurred, not how. We may be as we are because the biblical Eve took a bite of a fruit that was forbidden. Whichever way an individual feels comfortable believing, by way of either an instantaneous neuron change or a disobedient act, we came into being. Our first forbears were suddenly made capable of accumulating knowledge and acting upon the previously unrevealed concepts of good and evil. Because of Eve's curiosity or an unexplainable happening, we now send spacecrafts into and through outer space. A major shift in earthly command began. We were provided with the means to become masters of our lives and this miracle world."

He had said all of the above lightly, without

effort or emphasis. I watched as his face changed. He frowned. I felt he had made a solemn decision to press home what he was about to say next. I wasn't wrong.

With the utmost seriousness, he pronounced, "I believe that the advent of the human brain is equal to the birth of our Sun and its planets." He caught my eye before he continued. "I'm convinced that the origin of this singular mass of nerve tissue in our heads can be compared with the phenomenon that made it possible for life to form and thrive on our planet Earth."

All I could think was, "Wow! Our brain equal to creation itself?" I didn't know how to comment on that. So, after what I thought was a suitable and respectful interlude, I tried to bring the conversation down from the unexpected heights he had taken us. I said quietly, "Didn't we talk about how we had those matchless abilities, but didn't have a clue as to how to utilize them?"

The frown left as quickly as it had come. The solemnity lifted and he responded with, "Together we pictured our very early ancestors as orphaned children. Creatures with enlarged brains, but without fathers and mothers to teach them how to use this gift of superior intelligence."

"We speculated," I said, "on how we must have stumbled through a brutal period of trial and error. We saw mankind as weak, slow, lacking claws and teeth big enough to fight off larger and more powerful animals. Didn't we liken ourselves to prey rather than predator?"

Quinn nodded. "That we did. We also wondered how long our ancestors had to deal with their physical limitations before they compensated by inventing effective weapons and tools out of stone, flint and bone. No one as yet has decided the length of time it took for the earliest humans to level the playing field of survival. Human prehistory and our later chronicles of events indicate or symbolize progress. And our progress is the result of our overcoming any restriction that seemed to stand in our way. The very first tools and weapons had limitations so we created new and better ones. This process has never stopped. Once we were on an equal footing with the bigger, stronger and swifter competitors for food, this built-in force drove us to overcome all limitations. We moved from grunts to language, from the haphazard to the more organized. We advanced beyond constant bewilderment to a primitive logic that led to satisfying explanations for the things unknown and terrifying."

"You said the other day that despite our living by different traditions, et cetera, that we are essentially the same because of shared drives. Is this one of those drives, this refusal to be restricted?"

"It is the first of two. Both powerful. I'll talk about the second one later. The two are linked, but we can deal with them separately. If they were not a part of our nature, our enlarged brains could very well be wasted. They separately and together motivate us. It is because they drive us that our progress appears to have been inevitable. Our progress was not inevitable. It is due to something exclusive of our intelligence, our boon of free will. We had to be pressured to continually move forward. These two forces or drives did just that — drove us ever forward toward the future."

I recall Quinn frowning again. There was a period of silence that I didn't want to break. I waited. I could see him consulting some inner agenda. It was unusual for him to be this hesitant about anything he wanted to say. Finally, he seemed to have made up his mind and said, "I have so many examples of how we react to what we know or perceive to be restrictive. I want to be selective."

With just the beginning of a gleam in his eyes, he said, "I don't want to bore you to death."

I waved that aside and asked, "All of this has great meaning to you, doesn't it?"

"It does. I've thought about these things over a long time. I feel they're important. I feel pride in oneself is vitally important. That's not pride of race, accomplishment or position, I mean pride in simply being one of the human race."

"You have found that kind of pride? You take comfort in the fact that you're a human being?"

He smiled and said, "It sounds strange, but true. I feel we have an inner sense of our significance which we have trouble acknowledging consciously. A sense of our eminence is necessary before the drive to beat restrictions is implemented. We are monumentally important, every one of us."

I couldn't let that pass without comment, "I recognize the values you give us. I agree that we are singular beings, but we've had those who oppose your highly esteemed progress. Haven't we always had some who treasure the status quo?" I didn't wait for his answer. "Our accounts of past and present cruelty and the part that our inhumanity has played in our history must somehow figure in." I recall leaning forward, I suppose for emphasis, "I strongly object to some people, Quinn. Especially, those who spout our morals and then engage in the most immoral acts. I can easily despise those who use rhetoric to serve their own selfish ambitions. I mean how or why are all of us important or worthwhile? After all, there are killers among us and we can't forget the rapists, child molesters, bigots, psychopaths, and," I added, "the self-righteous."

There was no twinkle in his eyes now. Soberly he said, "No, I haven't forgotten the people who are responsible for our calamities and our torments." The twinkle returned as he went on. "If you'll just continue the patience you've always granted me, I'll get to our evil deeds and trans-

26

gressions down the road."

I tried for a touch of eye sparkle myself and feeling that I had failed, offered instead a slight smile and said lightly, "I'll be unwavering in my patience. It'll be hard, but I'll keep at it."

"Thank you." he said in the same light tone. The scowl reappeared. "Give me a moment or two. I've forgotten now what examples I was going to use."

"Sorry about that."

Absently, "No problem." He was deep in thought.

I waited quietly. I could guess what some of his examples might be. He had already sold me on our inbred resistance to limitations, but I was still interested. Knowing Quinn, I was sure there would be a few surprises.

He looked over and said, "Most of what I'm going to say is obvious once you think about it. The trouble is we don't give this incredible drive the consideration it deserves."

All I could do was bob my head as a sign of encouragement to push on. He did.

"Down through the ages we have routinely rebelled against any denial of what we now call human rights. Even if human beings could not articulate why they were enraged, they rose up against conditions they saw as intolerably oppressive. Somehow, down deep within us there is this conviction that we have an inborn right to certain irrefutable freedoms. This drive doesn't have as its goal turning us into simple pleasure seekers, but to insure that we do have, within reason, the freedom to control our own actions.

"Workers, angered by low, insufficient wages instigated by inflexible pro-profit or pro-business policies, will declare the employer unjust and strike for their fair share of earnings.

"Citizens under the yoke of a tyrannical regime will at some point initiate an insurrection, even though the odds seem solidly against success.

"Minorities have always found, either through mental skills or force, a way to battle discrimination—an overt restriction.

"We have to learn that blatant discrimination, prejudice or unfair treatment has never prevailed. The perpetrators of such actions against workers, repressed citizens or the most vulnerable minority groups have yet, over time, to maintain their self-righteous, self-approving position of power.

"The Soviet Union imploded because ordinary people were denied by a privileged hierarchy, their right to ownership, to live and work where they wanted, to advance according to their abilities. There was excessive censorship on certain books, music and art that was thought unjustified. Preposterous rigidity in public policies produced unacceptable limitations on personal growth and fulfillment. The rebellion in Moscow was not to gain privilege, but to live by those elementary rights we identify as human.

"I don't believe there is a paper that better justifies humankind's unqualified need for self-rule than our own Declaration of Independence. From Thomas Jefferson's inspired pen, all men were declared equal and endowed with an inalienable right to pursue life, liberty and happiness. With the utmost care he defies the repressive, unrelenting authority of a powerful king. The King of Great Britain is accused of establishing an absolute tyranny. Submitted to a candid world Jefferson lists the facts of imposed injuries and insupportable usurpation. This document, infused with beautiful language, creative thought and organized thinking, galvanized the peoples of America. No revolution had been so eloquently or scrupulously entered upon. It is a model or an established criterion for all principled insurrections."

Having been a long admirer of the "Declaration of Independence," I could only give my approval of his opinion and simple analysis of it.

His next example did surprise me. Not that it was inappropriate, but that he chose this one out of all the illustrations he had available.

I was getting used to his starting right in when he was finally ready. "These are people who were ostracized by society, and many were also shunned by their own families. They were ridiculed, called effete, made fun of endlessly. This small group of citizens was subjected to open contempt and harassment by the New York police. Back in the 60's, men and women were arrested simply for being in specific Greenwich bars. One June night the police again raided a bar called the Stonewall Inn. But this time a riot broke out as around two hundred patrons were thrown out into the street. Angry customers fought back flinging bottles, bricks and garbage cans. They were fed up with the obnoxious bias of the police and the unjust infringement on their basic right to be where they chose to be. The rioting continued for several days. This bizarre and unbelievable event was reported in newspapers and on television news programs across the country."

I said, "I remember the pictures and the hullabaloo that followed the riot."

"There was a lot of editorializing, more against than for the rioters."

I agreed.

He continued, "In spite of the adverse reactions, within weeks a social movement was under way. Organized gays and lesbians—those ostracized, ridiculed, held-in-open-contempt people— though small in number, sought to break down the social blockade barring them from the most rudimentary of human rights. It was a shock to hear them say that same-sex love was healthy and natural. However, that's what they promoted.

Imagine being in the homosexual posture while squaring up to the thousands who were against any change in their preconceptions or prejudicial one-sidedness. Nevertheless, they fought on stubbornly, advocating homosexual pride and self-affirmation. This tiny minority, tiny because many gays stayed safely in the closet, fought for their independence. They kept viable a pitched battle against those restrictions that attempted to deny them the right to live, for them, a positive lifestyle. It's hard, still, for some to accept the moderate success that had been achieved. For these anti-gay people refuse to see the courage involved. This, they may never accept, no matter its worth: Fundamentally, there is no difference between what took place outside the Stonewall Inn and in Tianamen Square. In both locations, there occurred a bloody engagement provoked by imposed, and, for the participants, unconscionable restrictions."

I wrote, before trying to recapture his recounting of the Greenwich Village incident and its consequences, that I was surprised by his choice. I was surprised only because his illustration involved sex, or more accurately, sexual preference. Of all the things we talked about, sex was never one of our subjects. I don't know why. Neither of us were overly modest or prudish. I can only guess that Quinn thought sexuality was private. I know I do, now that I think about it. How Quinn viewed the gay lifestyle, I'll never know. I can, of course, see that his focus was solely on a vilified minority fighting, against seemingly steadfast odds, for self rule. His reference to Tianamen Square had, I believe, nothing at all to do with a particular lifestyle. The human need to get past restrictions was his point. It was a good one. Personally, I didn't require another example.

Apparently, Quinn, too, was satisfied. He looked at his watch, got up and stood briefly in place flexing his knees after sitting so long. He said, "It's a little early, but I might as well go home and get prepared to hear how Bobbie did at her bridge." He chuckled.

He was through for the day. Small talk was clearly out of the question.

I got up, went through the same routine of being sure the legs were going to work as they should. ""Good stuff, Quinn. Very convincing. I'll look forward to the next bridge day."

His reply was a quick grin of thanks. He said, "See you later," as he headed for the door.

I wondered what our next session would bring. I didn't have long to wait. Sue and Bobbie had a Stac game at Polly's a couple of days later. They could not miss what, I've learned, is an opportunity to garner silver points for their climb to "life master" status in the bridge league.

CHAPTER 5

is his whole dignity and his wole merit.

Man is obviously made to think. It
is his whole dignity and his wole merit.

Pascal

The morning of "Stac" game day, Quinn called to suggest we have lunch at the Grill. We met there about 12:30 and found a place at the bar. Ron Horn, the friendly manager, came over to say, "Where have you two guys been? Haven't seen you in weeks."

Chatting with Ron was always a pleasure. He has a great talent for making you feel like very special guests.

In the Grill's clubby atmosphere, I ordered a vodka on the rocks. Quinn a coffee. We took our time before ordering the pasta dish of the day. Around the "U" shaped bar, people were eating and talking. We joined the pleasant buzz of amiable conversation.

Sated of food and geniality, we left about two hours later. Outside, as we turned on Granite Street to fetch our cars, Quinn said, "I'm talked out. When are the girls playing again?"

"I'm not sure. Probably next Tuesday at the Center."

"Unless they have something else planned before then, why don't we meet again at our house. Don't have lunch. Bobbie likes being productive in the kitchen."

I laughed. "I know. Tell her to go back to an old favorite. No experimenting."

Quinn matched my laughter and said, "The last time was a disaster, wasn't it?"

I could only subscribe to it being truly a disaster. "What was it?" I asked.

"I don't know. I do know there is no known recipe in print."

In memory of that meal, we exchanged more laughter on the way to our cars.

Driving home, I thought that he probably needed a little more time to organize his thinking. I wondered if he had finished with the human drive to overcome restrictions. I hoped that he'd move on to the second force. Naturally, I had speculated on what it might be and was curious to know if I had guessed right.

The following days passed uneventfully. On their bridge Tuesday, I arrived just in time to say hello and good-bye to Bobbie, who was on her way out. As I pushed through the door to the kitchen, Quinn greeted me with, "We're in luck. Bobbie made her foolproof quiche."

I could smell it and was delighted and said so. I had a weak vodka, Quinn his usual coffee.

We ate, comfortable in our familiarity. Small talk reigned. Then with dishes out of the way, place mats back in their drawer, we moved to the den. KAHM, the local FM station that played the "oldies but goodies," was tuned low. Quinn lowered the volume another notch and we each took our customary chairs.

"You ready for another... " he paused, trying to select an appropriate description. He came up with "session," the same as I had.

I said, "I've been looking forward to it. Carry on, Quinn."

Expecting me to say just that, he said, "I'm not quite through with our determination to triumph over those things that limit us. Too important to slight." After this announcement, he waited for my reaction.

I said, "Fine. This is your show. I'm here to listen."

Quickly, he said, "And comment when you feel like it. I want your observations or responses to these points I'm making. Or, struggling to make may be more correct."

Gently, "You can count on it, Quinn, and frankly, I don't detect any struggle at all."

"Okay," was all he said. He settled back and steepled his fingers with his elbows on the chair arms. I had never seen him do that before. It was professorial and just a bit out of character. From behind those hands he began.

"First, I would like to redefine human beings as I see them and, as I believe, we should all view ourselves."

The following were in his notes. I quote verbatim: "We are free of the control of nature or any other force unknown.

"We are armed with the faculty of reason. We have the ability to solve complex problems, to acquire and retain knowledge and to arrive at a long-range view of ourselves and the world.

"We are in possession of the genius to elect multiple choices and then make an independent selection.

"We have been given a godlike capacity to create. The splendid things we have devised are evidence of this extravagant gift.

"We are imbued with an incredible array of emotion. Some reward us and some punish us.

"When we recognize ourselves for what we are—when we are appropriately proud and respectful of ourselves, a latent force is released. We are then driven to overcome any restriction to our hereditary right to explore, right to think, right to conclude and the right to act upon our final judgments. In short, when we believe in ourselves, we impulsively take exception to whatever we perceive to be a limitation."

Though atypical, his notes from there on are remarkably complete—unlike so many others. I've decided to just continue as he wrote them, with this proviso. He didn't deliver these thoughts to me as easy-moving as he later put them down. That afternoon he sometimes caught himself unable to remember perfectly ordinary words that he was in the habit of using. It happens to all of us. It happens especially to those of us our age.

Other times he would start a sentence, sure of the point he wanted to make, then half way through lose the thread and be unable to finish it. He'd take a different approach and it would go well. Nothing more than commonplace absentmindedness.

Of course, in what he wrote, these hesitations, lapses or whatever one might call them, do not occur. Neither am I going to include my comments, which he duly put to paper. I feel they were in no way provocative, not the devil's advocate kind that provoke a spirited defense. I was simply supportive or encouraging—and, let's face it, dull!

These things he was saying to me and then later writing down, either seemingly in haste or at length, were the result of a long and abiding interest in human existence. Because of his conclusions, he had learned to worship life itself, but most particularly the human being. He had formed a philosophy, if that indeed is what it is, which though unschooled was a logical analysis of human conduct. His search for those principles underlying human conduct brought about a deep admiration—maybe worship is too strong a word—

of our species. Like no other I've known, he had found a way of reconciling himself with his time here on earth. Quinn had made his mind and spirit into what could be called a plausible harmony. He admired human beings for their resourcefulness and progress. Therefore, he admired himself. I know of no one more pleased with his life.

In all of our discussions, he strived to glorify all of us. There was never a question of his digressing from his central theme. He believed so strongly in our essential worth. He believed just as strongly that something of vital importance was missing in our lives when we failed to yield wholeheartedly to what he saw to be our indisputable significance.

I know he influenced me. In many ways, I am a different person. I think I'm a better person for having known and listened to Quinn.

It's hard to believe that his objective was to bring a greater understanding to just one individual. That individual being me. I can't accept that. He must have been preparing to reach out and bring his views to others. By way of his reasoning, make more people feel better about themselves and the whole of life, as I have.

His intent will never be known. His acquired creed, though, is so clear in what I will now copy, word for word, that one has to wonder for whom was this written message meant.

CHAPTER 6

Whatever there be of progress in life comes not through adaption but through daring, through obeying the blind urge.

Henry Miller

I have corrected some of his hurried spelling and punctuation, but basically here is what I found.

"Understanding this conscious urge to conquer what restricts, or simply appears to restrict us, helps tell us who and what we are. From our core centers, this inexplicable force emerges to push us out to unknown and previously unimagined frontiers. It is one of the keys to our intelligence turning into originality. Anything thought to be confining, an idea, thing, person or persons, doctrine or way of thinking, can be a catalyst to human creativity. It is this drive that has emancipated, elevated and refined us. This adamant compulsion can be called, simply, 'the human spirit.'

"We can hypothesize that the human spirit was there the instant those newly-formed genetic features took over. It may have been, but it has been from the beginning up to us to find reasons for self-regard or self-love in order to activate or release this life-fulfilling energy. We ignite our brains by somehow making a spiritual or intellectual connection with our divergence from all other living things. We then function in ways consistent with the human species' never-before-decreed sovereignty.

"A tiny change in our craniums and our eventual willingness to take advantage of that change, set us on a path of astonishing innovation and creativity. In a world and a universe that exists because of rules regulating conduct, our independent successes are truly awesome.

"To be awed—as we should—we have to remember that, even with our mental alteration, it took thousands of years for us to graduate from knowing only to search out and eat raw the roots and berries that nature provided. We don't know how long it took for our earliest predecessors to move beyond stalking and ripping open the throats of small prey and eating the flesh while it was still warm.

"After those primordial years, we gradually remodeled ourselves. We willed ourselves to overcome those things that hamper growth and, with a drive that said we should and could, we moved ahead.

"Because of the human spirit, we grew, and we learned as we grew and affected more and more changes.

"Some of our early family moved away from the security of easily-acquired shelter. They gave up a modest assurance of safety and sufficient food nearby. They were compelled to cross their own established boundaries and adapt themselves to different environments.

"Having learned to rebel against obvious limitations, they followed the unfathomable dictates of the human spirit. They bravely began to migrate. Though it is difficult to understand quite how they did it, our ill-equipped forebears eventually covered the globe.

"Tribes and extended families were inhibited by narrow sets of shouts or shrieked warnings, visual signs and gestures. Each group, at their own pace, developed sounds for things, words to qualify things, words to express feelings, and some words to glorify their world and the god or gods they believed managed it. The strictly human desire to get over the most difficult barriers provided us with verbal skills. The ability to convey what had been reasoned out increased proficiency and accelerated our progress.

"Human intelligence is an undisputed factor in all of our early accomplishments. But, so too, there had to have been a grasp of human significance in order for us to respond to this arousing force, the human spirit. In order to get past that which was perceived to be restrictive, there had to have been a powerful sense of identity. If

41

there was not, why would we test what was strange or invent that which was not a part of yesterday's experience? For whom but our deserving selves?

"About 15,000 years ago, we recognized our inability to make permanent our daily impressions and observations. Taking on that limitation, we painted images of animals on cave walls in France, Spain, Africa and Scandinavia. We recreated shaggy ponies, stags, bisons and wild cattle. Deep in stalactite-blocked caves, we secretly proved ourselves to be image makers. Hidden from view, away from the daylight and strangers, the pictures of moving animals had some of the reverential mystery of life itself.

"The spectacular works of prehistoric peoples were first discovered accidentally in 1868 by a nobleman hunting on his estate in Northern Spain. Seven years later a local landowner began a more intensive exploration of the Altamira caves. He was astonished by the vivid paintings. Though an amateur, he published what he considered the work of paleolithic man to a world of doubting scholars.

"The Altamira paintings remained in disrepute until 1902—some 20 years after other cave paintings across Western and Southwestern Europe were confirmed to be the works of paleolithic artists. Credibility finally brought recognition to the landowner, who died in 1888, and fame to Altamira, the nobleman's astonishing first discovery in Spain.

"However these paintings and exquisite drawings came to be, at the turn of this century we had to revise our view of prehistoric people's creative powers. Before they could write or were civilized, they moved from inventing what was wholly utilitarian to what was a permanent rendering of those things beautiful or important to them. The reasons for creativity, the reasons the human spirit dictated, remained the same, but the end product was startlingly different. A whole new aspect of human life unfolded in a universal microsecond.

"We had met the need for tribal communication and had created ingenious representations of the commonplace. Then, centuries later, we established a most important milestone alongside the roadway of human history. We brought about this most influential event by prevailing over the inefficiency of having to both hunt and gather our food.

"The origination of sowing and reaping provided a scarcely conceivable security and inevitably greater freedom. With the mission of survival to an increased degree now more under control, we slowly began examining other limitations and indulged in the pleasures derived from letting our imaginations rise above the needs of survival. As the centuries ran their course, with the help of language and the precious time to imagine, little was now beyond being challenged and often mastered.

"With an ever-increasing faith in our capabilities, our more recent ancestors began collecting noteworthy information and passing it on. But our memories were put to the test and found to be wanting. Our brain was unequal to what we asked it to store away. Upon recognizing that memory was held to certain limits, we invented word pictures so we could more readily recall things previously noted. Soon the pictographs and hieroglyphics became too narrow in scope. We moved on to a variety of marks that evolved into complex, but managed, alphabets.

"Every tribe or group, wherever they were and wherever they came from, met the need for human expression and produced a language. No one group failed to meet this need. Some, not all, went further and created those symbols and combinations of symbols that represented words and, thus, a chronicled history was introduced.

"We are told that stone tablets were put to use, but were obviously too heavy and too cumbersome. We solved this problem by resourcefully turning papyrus plants that we soaked, pressed and dried into light, easily storable and movable writing material.

"With this development, our experiences, disasters, vices and our follies became grist for our early writers. As adroit witnesses, they offered a record of our tragedies, sometimes our comedies, but always, knowingly and unknowingly, our grandeur. As creators, their personal impressions gave birth to modern literature.

"Our resistance to boundaries is beautifully expressed in music and painting. Undoubtedly distressed by only the clapping of hands or the beating of a crude drum, we invented elemental instruments and brought the different sounds together, creating music consisting of a single melody. Small groups of musicians grew into larger ones and over time whimsical embellishments were added. Slowly, we invented various simultaneous parts and the revolutionary idea of basic harmony was introduced. We created great orchestras and great symphonies to test ourselves. Each symphony was a challenge to create another, and another! We strived and became technically skilled virtuosos, interpreting our deepest feelings by combining a number of independent, but harmonizing, melodies and tones.

"When visual artists in the 19th Century grew weary of only reproducing nobility, religious figures, wealthy merchants and somber landscape scenes, they concentrated on light to the exclusion of subject. They moved on to a lighter palette. Soon the new 'impressionism' imposed its own form of suppression and a movement in painting characterized by nonrepresentational composition was born. Each new approach was a revolt against the old.

"We can see our ancestors leaping, skipping, jumping up and down to a hypnotic beat. Their bare feet stirring up the dust of what were probably ceremonial areas. We should really think of them and reflect on human progress when a ballerina floats gracefully across one of our many stages. We should honor human development when a ballet company performs with gestures and movements of precision and fluidity.

"In the area of practicality, a century ago we saw that the horse was too slow, too inconvenient, and the buggy it pulled, too cold in the winter. We fought those limitations and created the motorcar. In its early stages, it was still too slow, required unusual skills to change the movement or direction and there was no protection from the rain and freezing temperatures. Typically, we were urged to bring about solutions to discomfort and to built-in limitations. We made bigger and better engines and made the vehicle itself easier to operate. So this marvel would not be limited to a few, we initiated the production line and more people were able to transport themselves at speeds beyond the horse. To curb discomfort, we enclosed the vehicle with glass and invented a traveling heater. Today our heaters and air conditioners are thermostatically controlled, windows are made to glide silently up or down at the touch of a button, and, so as not to be confined to just driving, we talk business on our cellular phones.

"Just yesterday it seems, we, with the collective powers of our intellect and ingenuity—while being prodded by self worth and the human spirit—invented that thing that allows us to store in one file drawer all pertinent public records, documents, private papers of documentary interest and institutional records. Amazingly, this machine can also see infinitely more than we can, and it sees it quicker. It discerns more details, makes unheard of connections, corrects itself, learns unconvential skills, instantaneously produces three-dimensional images and much, much more. And we cannot forget that it allows individuals to develop contacts, or exchange information electronically 24 hours a day.

"This latest electronic marvel best represents our compulsion to overcome any combination of limitations, including our own, and establish a wholly new sophisticated way of life."

Quinn wrote well. He had the ability to make his thinking clear. What I don't understand is why all of his notes weren't as complete. Obviously, he didn't die deliberately, so maybe he did intend to write a paper or perhaps a book. Sounding me out may have been a preliminary step. Talking it out may have been his way of preparation. Thinkers do have their different approaches to self clarification, I'm sure.

Anyway, what I've copied covers two of our

meetings. Both for some reason were shorter than usual. The words brought him back stronger that ever. I recall so much. His gestures, his deliberations. His often silent thank yous, simply for listening. This charitable man had a grand and lofty purpose in mind.

CHAPTER 7

Life is a petty thing unless it is moved by the indominable urge to extend its boundaries.

Jose Ortega Y Gasset

Our next meeting was not detailed like the prior two. These notes are sparse, only an outline at best with his thumbnail sketch before me, I clearly remember how he began and his progression. Parts of what follows will not deviate from his main ideas, but the language will be, by necessity, mostly mine.

After moving to our habitual places in the den and getting comfortable, he said abruptly, "Permanently embedded in the modern psyche is the phrase 'all men are created equal.' It has penetrated most societies and those governments with harsh and unbending policies." He paused and said, "Actually, to be correct, it should be all <u>persons</u> are created equal. 'All persons' doesn't have the same ring, though, does it?"

I responded, "That's probably the reason we don't use it. But, don't you think that in today's world we know 'all men' means to encompass both men and women?"

"I suppose you're right. Still, it does bother

me whenever I read or say it. I'm sure it bothers others, as well."

"It may, but there's not much we can do about it." I smiled, as I recall trying to ease my too-readily-accepted defeat on the subject.

He answered my smile with one of his own and we were past further discussion regarding "men" versus "persons."

He resumed saying, "Being equal is the important thing. By acceding to equality, it is fitting for anyone and everyone to compete. Being free to match abilities or particular strengths liberates, to a greater degree than ever before, our second governing force. Looking forward to another opportunity to compete is now common to both men and women. Do you know what this second, powerful drive is?"

Another smile, "Is this a quiz?"

"No, no. I'm just curious."

"Well, naturally, I've given it some thought. But I've no firm choice."

He said, "For me, it is a force that has us aspire."

He was watching to get my reaction. Though I was puzzled, I said neutrally, "Aspire?"

"Yes, aspire. You know, to pursue or aim at a goal."

I said, maybe a touch defensively, "I know what aspire means. But aspire to what? When we are driven to overcome a restriction, isn't a goal involved? Aren't the two the same? To pursue a goal or to reach an objective by surmounting something strikes me as being initiated by the same drive."

"I know you'll recall that several weeks ago I said the two can be linked."

"I remember that."

He nodded. "You're right. Every effort to get the better of a limitation has a goal. This drive can also have us objectifying something that has nothing to do with constraint."

I thought about that for a moment and said, "You've lost me. I'm afraid you'll have to explain. I'm not altogether sure I understand."

Without hesitation, he said, "You've watched the Boston Marathon on television, haven't you?"

Baffled, I was more or less positioned to ask the question, "The Boston Marathon?"

I knew he was having fun with me, but he carried on pretending not to notice my surprise. "That is an international event. Athletes converge on Boston by the hundreds. They are there to run a long, grueling race; not to overcome something limiting, or to take a stand against, say, discrimination. They come without an agenda of defiance. They respond to an open invitation to match strengths. They aspire to take part in a competitive trial of foot speed. Nothing more."

"Some are there only to win."

"Some are, of course. The top conditioned,

the most fully trained, the most ambitious to reach the ultimate in personal elation. It is always exhilarating to win."

"Only one man and one woman can win. What about the second, third and fourth finisher? Won't they be disappointed?"

"If they're great competitors, they will be disappointed. But the important thing is they aspired to enter a contest and compete against the best the world has to offer. There has to be satisfaction in that. Not at first maybe, but later on. And some of those finishing in the top twenty or thirty will go home to train even harder. They will <u>aspire</u> to return and compete again."

"Okay! What about those who only finish in the first hundred or the first five hundred, or finish at all? What about those who finish hours later in the dark and are barely able to walk?"

"It's those people who make this race such a great metaphor for the human race."

"How's that?"

"True, there are hundreds of people entered. A vast majority know they stand no chance of crossing the finish line first or even in the top twenty. Still they train and look forward to the big day. They all aspire, but to different levels of achievement. They are all there to achieve their own sense of attainment. For some, it is just being a contestant. That's fulfillment enough. Others trained to just cross the finish line, however they manage to do that. They are all in Boston to achieve. We humans are driven to achieve. Our achievements can differ, but the satisfaction from a personally selected goal can be equal to another's whose goal is more ambitious. Human beings are dedicated to an urge to succeed."

I said with a semi-doubtful attitude, "So the human race can be compared to a marathon?"

"It can, but that's not our whole human story. We have individuals who compete with themselves. Whatever it is they hunger for, they try to reach it in individual degrees of perfection. They are those who are true to themselves and to their own vision. People who aspire to be better than they were."

"An example? I'm sure you have one."

"A very good one to start: Vincent Van Gogh. He stuck to the vision he had of how a finished canvas should look. He received no recognition. We are told he never sold a painting. His health failed, yet he carried on producing one great, innovative painting after another. He aspired to depict people and landscapes his way. He succeeded time after time. With a wet, completed painting, in a style of his alone on his easel, he must have had a momentary sense of immense achievement. Why else would he have continued? He was determined to succeed according to his own dictates. He as-pired to paint his way and his way alone. We have his works attesting to his vision, to his determination and to a human being who was a genius."

I said, "When the Getty Museum finally hung his work, titled 'The Irises,' Sue and I drove up the coast to Malibu to see it and the museum itself. I don't remember what astronomical amount of money someone paid for it, over 50 million, I think. I know after that sale, there was a default problem and Getty acquired it a couple of years later. Anyway, we stood a distance from the painting with a number of other people. The museum guards wouldn't let you get too close. Sue and I were mesmerized. The power of the man was there. I felt overwhelmed. The experience was truly magnificent."

"I believe what you were open enough to experience was the power of human purpose or aspiration. It is, like so many other things that make us unique, a human ability to admire another's achievement. In the case of a Van Gogh painting, it is more powerful because we know of his troubles while creating. Our admiration, with this knowledge of hardships endured, can be more intense."

"I suppose you're right. None of that went through my head that day. I simply gave in to his astonishing and wholly captivating accomplishment."

"What you've just said is tremendously important."

"How?"

"Well, there is only one Van Gogh, as there was only one Isaac Newton, one Buddha, one Albert Einstein, one Aristotle, one Shakespeare, one Beethoven, one Picasso, one Marie Curie, one Jesus Christ, but there are millions upon millions who respect, value and praise those of us who influence or create change. There are millions upon millions of admirers and that, too, tells us a great deal about the human species. Most can't match our geniuses, but we have the ability to recognize their brilliance and hold them in exceptionally high regard. We appreciate another's creative powers, insight, imagination, invention and ingenuity. We live by their authority. Those below the positions of genius or outstanding talent are proud of those who have perfected their talent. Probably, not one person in a packed concert hall could ever expect to play the violin like Itzack Perlman. Hundreds of people pay a high price for their tickets to be affected strongly by his dexterity, his pure tones, his interpretation of some other genius' musical composition. We are magnificent because we produce superb individuals and respect and praise them for their singular efforts to fulfill themselves. Their grand attainments become ours to cherish."

"What about the Guinness records?"

"Excellent, I hadn't thought of that. The Guinness record book, of course, shows to what lengths a human being will go to accomplish something. Anything!" He liked that and went on. "The records people set may be bizarre or silly, but still they're feats of which individuals can be proud. And," he had a tiny smile, "their names are in print for the world to see." He stopped and then, "Good thought, John."

"Thank you. Anyway, you're saying," I started slowly, "we don't have to be one of only the few who are blessed with abnormal skills or a capacity to develop imaginative creations," I hesitated before, "to be significant." I looked over at Quinn. "Is your point that we are all extraordinary because as humans we are capable of being extraordinary?" Another pause, "Are those who are not exceptionally creative just as exceptional because they are able to appreciate another's extraordinariness?" Knowing that was muddled, I said, "Did I really say that as badly as I think?"

He waved that aside. "It doesn't matter how you said it. You hit the nail on the head."

I stretched and said, "A carpenter, I am not, nor am I a wordsmith, but as long as we understand each other, that's what counts."

Another minute smile precluded our getting too serious again soon, but he did say, "Do we understand each other? My marathon analogy didn't throw you?"

I laughed. "It sure was unexpected." I thought for a moment and continued, "There are probably dozens, maybe hundreds, of ways you could have made your point. I think using the marathon was a good choice. Once I got over my initial surprise, it made sense."

Just then Bobbie bounced in. "Hey, you two still at it?" She looked at her watch and said, "I know it's only four o'clock, but is it too early for a glass of wine?"

We said, indeed, it was not. Quinn asked before she turned to leave, "How'd you do today?"

"Not too good," she said easily. "We were speedy, but weren't lucky."

Quinn winked at me and said, "I thought bridge was all skill. How does luck figure in?"

"My dear, do you have to be told that luck enters into all of our endeavors?" With a grin, she left.

Quinn watched her go. His smile faded slightly when he said, "Let's have our wine while I finish up. I've got a couple more things to say before we call it quits."

"Fine."

Bobbie returned with two lovely, stemmed glasses. "Mother's good crystal will make this economical Chardonay taste like high-priced stuff." She handed each one of us a glass and bounced out.

We took the first obligatory sip. Quinn put his glass carefully on the coffee table and said, "'By their fruits we shall know them.' That's from the New Testament's Matthew."

I nodded. "To you it means, by our achievements we can know ourselves?"

He agreed and went on with, "We think highly of our achievers. We want to know who or what has arrived at or near the pinnacle of success. We have weekly lists of the best selling books. There are the Academy Awards. We are fascinated by who will be voted the foremost actor and actress of the year. Best picture is a category that holds great interest. Our interest in the Emmy, Grammy and the Obie special selections parallels that of the Oscar award.

"Many of us, while in a strange town, want to know where its finest restaurants are. The Nobel Peace and Pulitzer Prize winners are universally acclaimed. A mystery novel has us guessing, but the stalwart character who fingers the guilty party is much admired.

"Champions of all kinds occupy us, most of whom worked hard to achieve. Though riches often accompany championships, most of us don't envy the title holder's good fortune.

"We form deep attachments for all our heroes. If one of them should be publicly shown to have clay feet, some of us will resist knowing it. We can be forgiving of our fellow paragons. We will resist the truth.

"Human beings are special, unique, majestic, because we are capable of going beyond what exists. We are transcendent beings because we love to achieve and do achieve. We surpass ordinary life because we also value those who attain their desired end. We find immense pleasure in being a fan. A roaring, approving crowd in any one of our many stadiums indicates just how much pleasure we get when a goal is scored or a player crosses home plate."

After that, we sat quietly drinking our wine. I had a lot to think about. I speculated on what his future topic would be, but not for long.

He said, "When the girls have their next match, I'd like to explore your evil doers who appear to run counter to all that we've talked about."

I replied, "I'll look forward to that." I admired the crystal and, with my new perspective, the human being's ability to produce such a beautiful thing. I took a last sip and placed my glass just as carefully, as had Quinn, on the table between us. Quinn got up as I did and followed me to the kitchen. En route I called out a good-bye to Bobbie. She shouted from a distance, "See you later, John." Quinn and I parted at the door.

I left feeling good and not because of Bobbie's "economical" Chardonay. Stimulated by the afternoon, I drove home.

I have condensed the afternoon's discussion. It's essential meanings or aspects are, I believe, unimpaired.

CHAPTER 8

Violence is essentially wordless,
and it can begin only where thought and
rational communication have broken down.

Thomas Merton

The night before our next scheduled get together there had been a late Spring powder ing of snow. I learned this when I went out to get the Phoenix morning paper, the Arizona Republic. It was still dark. Daylight was about an hour away. I read the paper, had my cup of coffee.

When I looked out the window, I expected the sky to be gray and hanging low over the whitened trees promising more snow. The sun had yet to appear, but the sky was cloudless and already a pretty blue. After Sue and I had our breakfast, I bundled up and went for a walk.

The sun was slowly warming the cool morning air. As I walked, leaving footprints on some of the still pristine sidewalks, I thought about Quinn. I remember thinking how extraordinary my meetings with him were. Possibly even a little strange. Knowing him well from our two-year plus association, I hadn't expected him to be so preoccupied with one subject, or speaking at such great lengths. He was a thorough man, but this laying out of his thoughts so painstakingly, omitting nothing, was truly astonishing. Our conversations, as I said earlier, were always far ranging, always skipping from topic to topic.

I trudged on, enjoying the covering of snow that would be mostly gone by noon. Quickly, my thoughts turned back to Quinn. I had known he was a compassionate man, a man with deep feelings about many things. He cared about all of the critical issues that we should all be concerned about: the environment, the state of government, education, et cetera. I compared the two of us for a moment. Where I was prone to be quite passionate—and vocal—regarding some of the country's disputed issues, he was without exception calmly analytical. He, I concluded, was a tireless, seemingly uninvolved, observer. I couldn't recall ever seeing him wrought up or outwardly vehement about anything.

But, I asked myself, could he be a raging volcano inside with never a ripple on the surface...?

Putting that aside, I supposed that his caring grew into an all encompassing involvement with the whole of the human race. Being an intuitive evaluator, he had, over time, developed a very special view of the human being. Then having found incomparable value, I guessed that he probably came up with a lot of concerns about why there was so much pain in the world. Why human "evil doers" were forever plaguing the rest of us. I saw clearly that he believed that human beings are to be revered. So, I wondered, how is he going to deal with those humans who bring us so much grief?

It was getting warm. I unbuttoned my coat, remembering that Quinn was going to have lunch with Bobbie and then come to our house around 12:30. As I walked on with coat flapping, I went over some questions that had been bothering me for several weeks. In the snow, under a brilliant sky, I prepared myself to ask those questions.

The morning past quickly enough. Small chores occupied me. Sue and I had finished lunch when Quinn arrived. We exchanged the customary pleasantries, got comfortable and he started right in.

He had a lot to say this particular afternoon and was eager to begin. In some instances, that day's observations are detailed in his notes. Others are barely acknowledged, but the slightest of hints bring back a flood of memories. Not only do I remember quite well what he said, but I have read with interest the books to which he referred. Therefore, I feel even more qualified than usual to record this afternoon's long session.

He said, "I'm sure you've been itching for me to get to those who bring so much torment into our lives."

"I have, I admit." I went immediately to my

62

thought-out questions. "What about the neighbor-hood bullies, the terrorists who use fear and blood-shed to intimidate? What about the hate crimes? The malicious killings of human beings by other human beings?" I hurried on. "What I find hard to understand is, if it shows good judgment to be decent, kind and rational, why are there so many who are not. Why are there these hundreds of per-petrators of violent acts performed in a manner that says they are for the sake of violence alone? You have made the point that we strive for perfec-tion, then why do some work hard at being a fail-ure? Why is there such hate and hostility when, as you say, it is so blatantly clear that the human race is unquestionably peerless and unthreatened in our sovereignty?"

"Big questions that deserve answers. Before we get to explaining our hostility, I would like to add to your 'whys'. Why are there men and women who want to crush another so completely they'll never rise up. Who want to witness other human beings submit unconditionally. Their victims are defenseless children, spouses, people in minority groups. Why?

"And there are the rapists. Men who really take their pleasure in shutting off a woman's ap-peal for mercy. Domination, absolute domination is their goal. We are able to understand their need for sexual release, but, for them, sexual satisfac-tion is only an adjunct, it is now claimed.

"Why must some human beings dominate so cruelly? Why would some people want to destroy another person's property? A person they don't even know? Why is there fraud that costs unsuspecting people their life's savings?"

I remember him saying, "On our list, some villains can also be victims."

That stumped me. I could only ask, "How's that?"

"Suicide is a case of villain and victim being the same person. Dope addicts and alcoholics are self-made victims. And, as victims, they are too often prone to committing malicious acts against family, friends and sometimes strangers." As if in total wonderment, he asked, "Why would anyone want to kill themselves? Why do some need a mind-altering, highly-destructive drug to get through an ordinary day? Why do so many muck up their lives by thinking that they have to be inebriated in order to perform well?"

I added, "Women go to school to get permits to carry guns just so they can walk the streets during the day. A female alone at night in a car or on a street is a rare sight—even in our small towns or on college campuses."

"Yes, and protective iron bars on windows are commonplace. Drunks accost us. Their alcoholic bravado, though more often than not counterfeit, is still full of risk. Youngsters are now just as threatening as hostile adults. We try to guard our homes and places of business with expensive burglar alarms, trained dogs and steel-cased dead bolts. Why do you think we have to live this way?"

"I'm not sure I know. Do you really have an answer to all of our whys? To evil that is so pervasive?"

Quinn wasn't ready to answer quite yet. "Your 'evil' shouldn't exist anymore," he said. "Not in a time of our psychological growth, of our more practical understanding of human behavior. But you're right, violent crime does appear more pervasive." He hesitated and then said, "Maybe it just seems that way because there are more people populating our world than ever before. As a consequence, wouldn't that mean that there are more people capable of violent deeds?"

I couldn't help but ask, "Are you suggesting that despite different situations or circumstances people are always behaving the same? I'm not sure a greater number of people should routinely mean an increase in violence."

With a frown on his somber face and a shake of his head, he said, "Sorry, that was something that just jumped into my head. Like you, now that I've thought about it, I'm not certain that more people necessarily insures more violence."

After another short bout of reflection, he said, "I'm sure of this, though: Television has expanded our awareness of violence. That may account for our feeling it is so pervasive. Atrocities from around the world are beamed into our homes twenty-four hours a day. Via satellites, far-off horrors that once would have taken place unannounced are now seen in televised color, sometimes as they're happening."

I said, "I know that I've seen and read enough of senseless shootings, clubbings, bloody bodies and seen too many tortured faces of children."

"Television has made us more aware of our sadistic treatment of each other. I'll ask you this, do you think you're less affected emotionally having seen so much of violence or its aftermath?"

"I never thought about it, but sure. Brutality is almost commonplace. I've learned to expect a certain amount of it on every newscast."

"Shouldn't we be concerned that, generally speaking, we are less sensitive to the suffering of others? Because it's 'commonplace,' aren't we hardened to tragic events?"

"As individuals, I'm sure we are." I stopped. Suddenly I had something pop into my head. I said, "Maybe there is another perspective to the common use of satellites by television news." I took my time and finally said, "This may be weak, but let's consider it anyway."

"Don't qualify, John."

I smiled. During the short period of silence that followed, Quinn sat quietly waiting. When I was ready, I said, "At the time Hitler first initiated his militant persecution of Germany's Jewish citizens, word of his pogrom's appalling viciousness was meager—outside of German, that is."

"I believe few outside of Germany knew of its scope."

I nodded and said, "If there had been hand-held cameras and satellite dishes and the news media was the size of today, might not his pursuit of such extreme evil have been cut short? If the world, through television, had witnessed the Nazi's barbaric attack on defenseless citizens, would not there have been an outpouring of condemnation? My point is, if there had been televised coverage, maybe Hitler would have been stopped and the world wouldn't have been engulfed in a senseless war with its mass killing."

"You're justifying the showing of violence in our homes?"

"I guess I am." I hastened to add, "But only the well grounded, as contrasted to fictional violence on some of our crime shows."

We both thought about the reverse side of television for a moment or two before I asked, "Would Stalin have been able to carry out his starvation of peasants and terrible purges if there had been vivid pictures and lucid commentary revealing his ordered atrocities?"

"I believe the Soviet Union was already a closed country. How would the news people obtain access to do their reporting?"

I answered quickly, "I believe they would

have found a way. Any news, especially that which is startling, is irresistible to the news industry. Any leak is followed up. The people in the business of broadcast news are relentless in their dedication to gathering and projecting shocking communiques by way of words and pictures."

He considered this for another moment and said, slowly, "The point you're making could be a valid one."

I acknowledged his comment with another small smile. "I'll finish with Kuwait and Bosnia as examples of the networks and cable doing, with no ulterior motive, what is simply their job. The Iraqi invasion of Kuwait and its inevitable destruction dominated the world's screens. Everyone with a set saw what was happening. Ordinary people, along with powerful representatives of nations, reacted. Within days, Desert Storm liberated Kuwait and Hussein's troops were routed. Without the televised display of Iraq's brutal onslaught, would the reaction time have been as swift?"

Quinn interjected, "And when Kuwait's oil fields were shown burning in Hussein's retaliation for his humiliating defeat, most of the world felt justified in the sudden and thorough punishment of Iraq for its aggression."

"If justification was needed, those appalling pictures furnished it. Is it possible that television will prove to be our deliverance from another World War?"

I waited for a reaction. There was none, so I said, "Without the pictures of civilian corpses and women and children being killed in Saravejo's streets and market places, would NATO with its air strikes, have intervened to the extent that it did? We were told that the situation in Bosnia was hopeless, a deadly trap that Europe and the United States didn't want to fall into. The sickening pictures and the chilling commentary kept coming, however. Finally, at great risk, the bloodshed was brought to an end. Diplomacy and strength of purpose, despite the promise of a deeper involvement that no one wanted, prevailed. Credit may be given to television for making known and making memorable the slaughter excesses, excesses that could hardly be ignored. If the wanton killing had preceded the science of transmitting pictures or scenes, the ethnic cleansing might have continued with a much longer and bloodier result. Could we have avoided another major conflict because of CNN's almost continuous coverage? We may be less sensitive as individuals to the violence we see on our television screens. But if dramatic pictures of crimes against humanity anywhere on the Planet energizes nations into immediate action, then television must play a positive role in world affairs."

"Your point is well taken." Thoughtfully, "Perhaps we should learn to be less critical of television."

"If I'm right, the UN or an international court of arbitration might not accomplish any more than the televised reporting beamed into millions of homes and dozens of capitols. Television may not be the answer to a truly civilized world in the twenty-first century, but maybe we can think of it as an added factor in our never-ending search for peace."

Quinn seemed deep in thought. I decided to change the subject. "We can talk about the impact of television some other time, though." I said, "Let's get back to your people who play such a huge role in today's violence."

"If you want to, fine! Your analysis is too interesting not to talk about further."

"We will later. Right now, I'd like you to continue." I went on with, "Before I started all of that, I was going to ask you about low self-esteem. I've read a lot about how self-doubt breeds violence."

"Indeed, we all have."

"Isn't it believed that people who feel that they are not in charge of their lives, find satisfaction through destructive acts over which they do have control?"

Quinn, though still somewhat distracted, endeavored to gather himself. He was staring past me out the window. Glancing back and catching my eye, he said, choosing his words carefully, "There are behavioral professionals who are convinced that our not feeling good about ourselves is so painful that we are compelled to inflict pain on others. These behavioral scientists are sure that if successful in causing others to suffer an equalizing pain, the triumph is a powerful boost to weakened egos and brings about an experience that is pleasurable."

Still a little disconnected, he reached into his shirt pocket and took out three neatly folded sheets of notebook paper. The same kind of lined paper he had used for the notes I have. Taking his time, he unfolded them. He smoothed out the creases as best he could. Their order was reversed and he finally looked up and said, "I found a book in the library titled," he glanced down, "Escaping the Hostility Trap, written by Dr. Milton Layden. Dr. Layden offers a formula that, for him, sums up the reactions of the emotional system to insecurity." He looked down again and read, "I=A+OB+H+S+MAR." He couldn't help but smile, "Not something you carry in your head for ready reference."

"Hardly. What does it mean?"

Referring to what he had written, he said, "His 'I' symbolizes inferiority, the equal sign means it generates 'A' or anxiety. 'OB' stands for obsession with oneself. 'H' equals hostility. 'S' represents a mirage of superiority. 'MAR' designates martyring or putting the blame on another for one's own failures. This formula tells us that a person who feels inferior—for whatever reason—generates anxiety,

71

which leads to self-obsession, which can lead to hostility. The hostile acts make the individual feel superior, which is aided by a need to put the blame on others for how bad one feels."

I acknowledged the reasonableness of the formula now that it had been explained.

He went on to say, "Dr. Layden's purpose is to make clear how some, because of their insecurity, give themselves up to hostility. Now, I take hostility to mean feelings of ill will, of unfriendliness, et cetera, but not necessarily resulting in violence.

"No doubt, some people are impaired by a self-loathing. There are those who may not be fully conscious of their acute self-doubt or that they are driven by a compulsion to overcome it. For a number of years it was accepted that under acknowledged and undisciplined pressure these people often turn to senseless and hurtful ways to gain Dr. Layden's false mantle of superiority. To accomplish feeling better about themselves, they, for example, may form a bias toward a minority. Their intolerance becomes a means by which they feel and act haughty, condescending or patronizing. Or become aggressive and physically attack a member of that minority. To the low self-esteem advocates, both being scornful and resorting to violence brings about a sense of superiority. Each derogatory remark, each assault is a personal victory and momentarily they feel pride."

"I remember reading somewhere that through anti-Semitism any fool could become a member of the elite."

Quinn looked pleased and said, "That's new to me. I like it."

I smiled and asked, "Do you believe that raising self-esteem is the obvious way to end crime and brutal acts? Is crime and most such acts carried out by those plagued by self-doubt? Does Dr. Layden and do others hope to repair shattered egos and then sit back to watch human savagery disappear?"

"Lots of people believe, or believed, that that was the ultimate answer to human ferocity. And, too, educators have tried to link academic success to a student's self-confidence. Surely, adults can easily damage the confidence of their young charges. Parents and teachers should respect and encourage their sons, daughters and students. But some of those same people now question that low self-esteem always means scholastic failure as well as being a precursor for violence. Raising self-esteem was promoted as a way to end crime. And poverty was believed to be created by people who were too beset by doubt about their ability to work. Sounds good!"

"I see where it could be the cause of some crime, but hardly the only or chief cause. I certainly doubt that it's the single cause for poverty."

Quinn affirmed my opinion by saying, "There

have been innumerable people who were not content with themselves and found positive, life-supporting means to correct their negative image. In another book, <u>The Rage Within</u>, Dr. Willard Gaylin writes," he picked up his paper and read, "Equity and fairness are fundamental needs for peace of mind." He looked up, "There can be outrage when we are denied peace of mind and a competitive spirit takes over. It may drive an individual to assertive behavior. It can also drive some, he says," glancing down, "to perfection of skills, to creativity and high performance. That it has destructive aspects is only too evident in a competitive society gone haywire."

I said, "I suppose that some who don't like themselves find that defrauding others makes them feel in command—or superior."

"Right! The most pathetic is a grown person molesting a child. When we read about molestation, one wonders how this can possibly bring any satisfaction. It does, perhaps, for it is a control for those who have so little say over their own lives. Those who feel inconsequential may gain a certain satisfaction that makes them feel good."

I added, "It's easy to surmise that bullies are often beset by doubts about their own worth. Bullies try to disgrace anyone smaller or weaker than themselves, I would guess, to build up their shaky egos. If you have a healthy ego, this, too, is hard to accept. With a healthy ego, wouldn't there be no need to bully or dominate?"

He indicated that he was in agreement and continued, "We must endure both skilled and clumsy liars who must deceive to appear bigger or smarter than they are—to make themselves important in the eyes of others.

"Innocent people are threatened and, sadly, sometimes killed by a person who needs a gun to achieve an unfamiliar sense of power. Power for the unsure or the uncertain can be a mighty source for ego satisfaction. A sense of power can be even sexually stimulating. Inferiority can initiate a need for power.

"These actions are but futile attempts to regain or gain a sense of what everyone must agree to be a universal goal, that of self-importance.

"For those not affected with the steady pressure of self-doubt, it is difficult to appreciate what a tremendous burden it can be. The cost of feeling unworthy or incompetent is the stress of developing a personality alien to the human qualities that define us. We have persons robbed of sufficient judgment regarding the value in themselves or, in some cases, any part of humanity. Obsessive self-interest, an obsessive need to prove themselves worthy, may well govern their lives. But does it always lead to violence? Sometimes yes, but always?"

I remember saying, "I can support the view that some people lacking self-esteem may try to overcome it by hurting others. I can see drugs and alcohol as a means to forget one's trouble or to feel better about oneself. People, I'm sure, yield to drink to try and handle some private concern. I know alcoholism is now deemed a disease. It's obvious that our bodies react separately to stimulants, different medicines and drugs. But there has to be a reason for wanting to drink or do drugs in the first place. Drugs and alcohol can produce instantaneous effects. They can fill some with a sense of bizarre self-confidence. A temporary suspension of their problem or concern can happen. Users of narcotics can feel they know everything, understand everything and can achieve anything. The mystery of the universe can be a mere trifle. But I can also see that if one possesses self-awareness, one's identity is intact and that personal image is challenged, a protective reaction capable of bringing on violence can follow."

Quinn smiled and raised up slightly the sheets of paper that had been put back in his lap. "Another observation by Dr. Willard Gaylin is he feels that calling crimes 'crimes of passion' is wrong. He wrote that crimes of passion are euphemisms. They are more accurately crimes of humiliation."

Still consulting his notes, he said, "Freud believed we humans have a latent death instinct, which manifests as either a self-destructive drive or a drive to destroy others."

"That's hard to go along with."

"The majority of psychoanalysts don't. They find it more reasonable to believe that ferocity against oneself or others is not biological, but a reaction to outer stimuli. Explosive aggression, for them, is due to humiliating social, political and economic circumstances, all of which disgrace, degrade or shame some people. And those people are usually the impoverished or the oppressed."

He went on with, "Some people in our ghettoes are incensed because they believe society outside their urban area is unfair or unjust. Others might blame their economic situation on discrimination and obvious racial preconceptions. Government policies can be seen as barriers to their living up to expectations, whatever those expectations might be. Their lives are made up largely of apprehension, shattered ambition, resentment, quite a lot of hate, and very little hope. It's true, I suppose that they are further inflamed by their own inadequacy to deal with what they feel are unwavering restrictions. That doesn't mean, necessarily, that they feel inferior! They're mad, angry and at times enraged, and their raw indignation can end in violence.

"Street crime in the inner city and minority neighborhoods is the reason for most of our homicides. The isolated violence in our suburban neighborhoods has also been on the rise for years. But those numbers are negligible when put next to our urban violent crimes and homicides. Serial killers get the headlines, but such people are few and far between by comparison to those who commit other heinous crimes. We have to learn that most violent crimes are not conceived in diseased minds. When people realize they're nothing but second class citizens, things start to fall apart. Killing and looting, selling drugs, raping, fleecing and random bloodbaths may be the products of no jobs, little education and, of course, not much hope. When young people are excluded, when they've had enough of snubs and dishonor, they band together. They get comfort—the support we all need—and safety from being together. They understand each other's discontent, and they bond. We may find them arrogant and belligerent and intractable, but they are only being confident of their right to a place in this world and only standing up, albeit by stomping and crushing others, for themselves. The gang seeks power and finds it and seldom without resorting to criminal acts and violence."

He waited a moment and then said, "You know, John, there can be a great deal of gratification in losing your temper. You can derive pleasure from letting go, if you get away with it. A sense of certainty is possible. Rage can result in that which is so profoundly irresistible to the dispirited: power." He looked at me with the hint of a smile and said, "Power is so much more dazzling than money, or contentment or simple enjoyment, don't you think?"

Offhand, I didn't know what to say about that and said so.

He answered, "Nevertheless, this boiling over too often results in violence. It can be a living hell to feel you're on the outside and knowing that to those inside you don't count. It is torture to feel left out. It is agony to feel helpless or to be demeaned in ways that you know are unfair. Especially when you believe you have the right to the opportunities and all of the bits of happiness that are freely accorded the suburban majority. These embarrassments or mortifications are potent instigators of extreme resentment. Excessive resentment is a potent catalyst for exaggerated retaliation, an outrageous, contemptuous repayment for the shame and the mortification endured. Humiliation can be excruciating." He looked at me as if he were asking, do you understand just how painful?

Not waiting for me to say anything, he went on, "We humans have a whole host of ways, most of them destructive, to ease this living hell. Allowing rage to rule is just one. Finding an outlet for the inner turmoil makes one feel better. If that outlet is finding someone to shatter, he or she can experience a sense of self, or self-importance. The need to feel important is an acknowledged, all-powerful drive. If this drive is not satisfied, humans, unlike animals, can give up on life by way of suicide or drugs, or try to escape the torture of having been treated as if second-rate by whatever means at our disposal. There can be no doubt that feeling equal to others and, therefore, meaningful is essential to our having a positive outlook on life. And how do any of us feel equal or meaningful?"

I looked at Quinn and waited.

He said, "By knowing self-respect. And one indispensable contributor to our achieving self-respect, for most of us, is a show of respect from others."

I found that just a bit too simple. It was much later before I recognized how much truth there was in this uncomplicated and certainly not elaborate declaration of Quinn's. I copied his tendency of brushing something aside when I wasn't quite ready to deal with it and said, "I don't question that when one's self-respect level is disturbed, he or she can go immediately on the defensive. We all react when deprived of an essential need. But if we are deprived of what status we believe is deserved, when our sense of identity is challenged, I see how some can become absorbed by an abrupt or lingering urge for revenge. I've been angry when I've been humiliated or embarrassed. That's natural, but your position is that most of our violence follows an obsession with revenge or retaliation after humiliation."

"Yes, that is my position. Do human beings

who are free of never-ending degradation and have a healthy respect for themselves have to resort to waging war, killing and maiming others to feel worthwhile? Do they have a craving to terrorize or subjugate in order to feel significant or important? When we respect others and ourselves, must we seek out power for power's sake alone—a self-aggrandizing prestige? I believe that there is no need whatsoever for assuming a self-serving authority if one is in touch with their own significance and the signification of the human race. If people who value humankind find, because of certain capacities or aptitudes or learned skills, in positions of power, I believe they use that power to benefit others. I believe they are discerning and charitable when it is clear that they have the prerogative to make decisions affecting those around them. There is no doubt in my mind that those who believe in human value don't set out to dominate or destroy other human beings."

I nodded and said, "I see that. I see that someone without respect for themselves or others who achieve power can be more destructive than constructive. Without question, we have people who can't get enough power. It's just that it may take me a while to go along with the view that all of those who have an overwhelming need to prove themselves by dwarfing or controlling other people are the underlying cause of our most egregious problems. And that humiliation is the underlying cause of most violent behavior."

This didn't bother him nor slow him down. He glanced my way and said, "Let's consider again our inner cities. In our crowded ghettoes negative values are passed on from generation to generation. These negative values promote a sense of meaninglessness. Meaninglessness builds resentment and, in turn, bitterness and anger. Young people strike out. Why? Because they are, in their minds, restricted. They want to break the restrictions by conquering something or somebody that they feel is responsible for the imposed limitations. Ask any kid in a ghetto why he or she has a gun and the answer will be twofold. One, for protection. The safe answer. Two, no matter how they put it, the gun is easily achieved power—a release from helplessness. It makes them important. They feel in control of a part of their lives. A gun does a lot for the inner-city kid who feels helpless and hopeless."

Quinn had been leaning forward. He appeared to will himself to relax a little. Leaning back, he picked up his sheets of paper once more and again changed their order. He referred frequently to what he'd written and with little hesitation rattled off the following reasons why people turn violent:

"Chances are that those physically brutalized throughout childhood will grow up with a propensity to kill or threaten to kill. Cruelty reflects a lack of respect!

"If human beings are victims of constant disapproval—disrespect, they become antagonistic, often fiercely so.

"Kept from enjoying one's understood rights as a human being is invariably cause for hostility that can move up to bloodshed.

"Rejection is incredibly painful. Rejection can drive most anyone into a fury.

"If already insecure, any criticism will constitute disrespect and a threat. Faultfinding, denouncement, any manner of censure can initiate the need for a retaliation of some kind. Even in the secure, disapproval can be hurtful and must be dealt with. It is only ignored when one has sufficient self-respect and finds it totally baseless or petty.

"Questions raised regarding our essential worth can produce stress and induce a fierce response. Suggested unworthiness is unacceptable and must be somehow or other refuted.

"A questioning of one's competence is degrading. Open contempt can be unbearable. Both can become a challenge inviting a response case in the framework of violence.

"When individuals feel betrayed, or abandoned, they can be hurt and then outraged if they finally are persuaded that the betrayal was unjustified.

"Indifference and disdain can, when not

balanced by a sense of self-worth, produce out-rage.

"If trivialized, human beings without a sense of human value can be extremely volatile.

"I believe that humiliation is a factor in what appears to be censurable violence. With our understanding of human behavior, it is time we acknowledged that humiliation does not assure humble resignation. We must see clearly that it too often assures a dangerous retaliatory act of revenge.

"What does all this mean? It means no human being can for long bear, stand or tolerate being denigrated, belittled, denied acquired or endowed rights, discriminated against, shamed or shown open contempt. All of these things are fundamentally repressive. And it is against our nature to suffer limitations, as we've discussed."

Here, as I recall, he became quite eloquent. He no longer referred to his notations.

"Just as there must be a rationale for our constantly bringing fresh interpretations to all we see, hear and feel, there must be an explanation for our violent acts. Just as there is a rationale for our overcoming the status quo, there must be an underlying reason for never-ending human hostility, bitter rivalries and our always having lived with hatred and discord.

"I wonder how we moved from hunters and gatherers to indulged shoppers in attractive malls and still act like merciless barbarians toward each other. The answer lies, I believe, that we are even more the same than an organ transplant indicates. Every one of us on this planet who is not psychopathic, and is free of any of the various mental functional disorders, are more alike than we ordinarily believe.

"None of us can abide a suggested insignificance or involuntary feelings of irrelevance. We cannot willingly accept with acquiescence that we are meaningless. Anything that degrades can be intolerable. Disgrace has been unbearable as long as we have inhabited this earth. Human beings are simply not structured to be content in shame or in disrepute.

"When there is no dignity, no pride, not even simple humanity, some of us may exist solely to somehow escape the pain of feeling insignificant. Honor and self-respect are the often unrealized, but undeniable, goals of the human being. A sense or shame ignites a need to be worthy, if not of respect, then at least of affirmation."

His emphasis shifted a bit as he continued. It sounded as if he didn't know how to stop himself from talking. "The very strong may dismiss an attempt to shame or dishonor them. They may detect no reasonable basis for the attack and forget it. Some may recognize that a personal criticism has a basis and work to correct what may be a legitimate fault.

"Others, however, respond very differently. There are those who fail to make a stand against downgrading. They can quickly become depressed and fall into despair. If the despair becomes unendurable, they may resort to suicide or escape the pain through alcohol or drugs.

"There are those in the inner cities, however, who refuse to assent to downgrading. They intuitively sense their relevance and proudly reject feeling inconsequential. Their indignation is followed by anger and this anger growing into a fired-up rage is their only remedy. A developed righteousness has them retaliate. There is a great need of compensation for any attempt to humiliate. In distress, they try to bring an equal amount of humiliation to others. What they are seeking is a hold on a sense of identity through abusive and destructive acts. Their actions can be deadly, but never, no matter how brutal, do they achieve that which is needed most. Their efforts at revenge never succeed in bringing what they really need; a self-sustaining inner regard for themselves."

He switched the pages and looking at me said, "Dr. Gaylin once more: 'Withdrawal of love, deprivation, disappointment, exploitation and frustration are the beasts of the modern-day jungle.' His 'beasts,' it seems clear, are the principal instigators of nearly all of our explosive social problems. We must tame the 'beasts' before we can lose the contradiction in his 'modern-day jungle.' We must face up to certain realities before we can live as we should live, as we deserve to live.

"Degrading ourselves and others is a perversion of our preeminence. I am convinced that our intent and our responsibility are not to look upon any part of the human race as inconsequential or unimportant. When we do, we are committing the definitive crime."

Quinn was exhausted, and so was I. The afternoon had been very concentrated. A lot of thought had been squeezed down in those three sheets of paper covered with reminders. The thing missing was easily identified: What's to be done to end or diminish violence. I didn't want to bring that up. If he had a ready answer, I really didn't want to hear it. There was just too much for me to assimilate before tackling a solution, if there was one!

We sat quietly for a while. I looked at my watch. Sue would be walking through the door any time now. I said, "Would you like a drink? A scotch or a vodka?"

He seldom drank anything other than wine, but I wasn't at all surprised when he replied, "I'd like a scotch and water, John." I started to get up and he said, "Weak. Lots of water and ice, if you would, please."

He stayed seated, not moving. I returned with our drinks. I put his and the coaster that I had brought from the kitchen on the table by his chair. He said, "Thanks," and reached for the glass. After a few sips, he asked, "A lot to think about, right?"

I said, "A lot, Quinn. It'll take me a while to bring it all together."

There was a faint twitching of his lips. The barest beginning of a smile that didn't materialize. We drank our drinks slowly.

Sue came in, saw us still seated and called hello. We said, "Hi, how'd you do?" The usual greeting.

She answered, "Not sure. We'll find out later." Shrugging off her coat, she went into the bedroom.

Quinn finished his light scotch, got up and carried his glass and coaster to the kitchen. I walked him to the door. He looked tired, as well he should after his amazing performance that afternoon. "Oh," he said. He turned back just as Sue came out of the bedroom. He smiled at her and said, "Your husband is a great listener."

Sue replied, "Really? That's news to me."

We all laughed politely. Quinn said goodbye to the two of us and left.

I closed the door and turned back into the kitchen. Sue was waiting and said, "Quinn looks beat. Is he not feeling well?"

I responded, "He's fine. He had a lot on his mind today and getting it all out wore him down a bit."

"What was it this time?"

"I'll tell you later. I've got to first sort through what he said before I can talk about it and make any sense. I'll tell you this. It was a most interesting afternoon. He was extremely well prepared and very articulate. Everything he said was thought provoking. He's given me a great deal to think about."

With that we dropped the subject. We had our light dinner, watched the CNN news, Larry King, and then something else that didn't hold my interest. I went to bed early. I, too, was worn out and determined not to think about the consequences of low self-esteem or humiliation until later.

CHAPTER 9

What does reason demand of man—to
live in accord with his own nature.

Seneca

The following morning was cold. I went out in the dark for the paper and hurried back in. When there was daylight, I raised the window shades and looked up at a dull overcast that threatened more snow. I quickly decided, with only a slight twinge of disappointment, to forego my morning walk.

Sue and I had breakfast and watched the morning news. With our dishes in the dishwasher, I went to my desk. I wanted to review Quinn's dissertation—what else could I call it—on low self-esteem and humiliation and his far-ranging consequences.

He had so much to say, I knew it would be impossible to remember it all. I wished that I had put my Radio Shack tape recorder, which I hadn't used in ages, between us. But, how was I to know he was going to be so dumbfoundingly well prepared?

Well, I thought, you can't use that as an excuse, John. He's amazed you before by his thoroughness and ability to arrange and deliver his thoughts.

Setting aside blaming myself for not having enough foresight, I settled into trying to come to grips with what I could recall.

I was able to recognize that self-loathing could be a precursor to suicide. That was easy. I tried to go beyond that to the disintegration of a personality leading to a sense of isolation and a searing despair. I tried to measure the depth to which one experiences fear, or anger, or a crippling wound to one's feelings. Over the years I had been insulted, certainly ignored and a time or two shamed, and it was painful. I asked myself, was it just my good fortune not to seek revenge or have the need to escape the distress by way of drugs, or to contemplate suicide?

I thought, is this why Quinn's emphasis on debasement and self-doubt and their dire consequences hadn't fully convinced me they were the major problems he gauged them to be? Is it that I've never really hated anyone to that final stage of brutish assault, or felt restricted by a social hierarchy? Is it that I've never had to deal with a situation that was deliberately concocted to mortify? Or one that was an emphatic threat to my well being? I didn't know.

I know I was not as fully convinced as Quinn on the morning following his spelling out of how and why violence plays a constant role in our daily lives. As I write this, I have had the advantage of reading his notes, which included those three pages he brought with him that day. With those notes and the books I've read to help me, I have, to the best of my ability, organized and chronicled our discussions. So today I know this for sure: After the total experience, I am 100 percent influenced by my too-short friendship with Quinn. After months of working at recapturing those sometimes mind-boggling afternoons, I am a devotee of his and so many others' points of view, or their system of beliefs and values, relating to human behavior. My only qualification is that some of our destructive actions are due to a mental or pathological disorder and can't be assigned to injustice or to degrading or oppressive circumstances.

Human abnormalities surely account for some violence, but they are, I now believe, minimal in comparison to the monumental amount of violence initiated by people cursed by a low opinion of themselves or a driving need to retaliate for an uncalled for rude and scornful indignity.

Regarding a profound insecurity, I have become convinced that it can originate while experiencing the psychic effect of early trauma. That this trauma can spin a complex web or a carefully woven mental trap from which some rarely escape. I believe that the need to break loose from the web or trap can last a lifetime. That some human beings exist only to be free of their self-doubt and its attendant anxiety. For those so caught, life is truly a burden to be endured, not an unmatched privilege to be enjoyed. Think of the people you've known whose one ambition is to be liked and admired. What a crushing blow it must be to meet resistance.

I'm at that point where I would like everyone to believe that our human tragedies <u>are</u> the result of lost pride or a self-respect that has been challenged. I would like us to recognize that every human being has an overpowering need to have a feeling of pride in oneself. Our catastrophes originate in those trying to protect their identity or to achieve respect from outside themselves. Proper self-regard, however, must come from within and be whole and as close to being invincible as possible. Not everyone can rise above resentment and demand for revenge to show magnanimity. Only those supported by an inner security can do that.

There have always been people who see other humans as the enemy to be conquered. We have known how to chase them down after they begin hostilities, but we have not yet learned to solve their antagonisms before grievous damage has been done. What I found so difficult to accept is that they are people who have lost any or only temporarily lost contact with their inner grandeur and are trying to regain or compensate for the loss. However much we suffer from their outrageous conduct, we must, without making them too sympathetic, try to understand how much they suffer before trying to cushion their inner distress. None of us should be impaired by feeling insignificant. All of us should be suitably and consistently proud of who we are.

Going back to my morning of contemplation, I finished by wondering again if Quinn had any answers. Could he possibly have a solution to our bloodletting, our verbal, physical and substance abuse, our cruel disdain for others? Are there ways of dealing with those who are driven by a need for power before they exercise that power and destroy more lives? How can we make everyone see that power is for those who do not aspire to power? Is there any chance at all of saving those who bear the cross of suicidal despair before the wasting of a life?

I certainly did not have a clue to any viable, or inclusive solutions. I thought, if Quinn has gone this far in his study of violence, surely he has something pertinent to say about what we can do about the problem. I resigned myself to wait until our next session. Be patient, John, I told myself. It didn't do much good.

CHAPTER 10

We feel good and ill in proportion
to our self-love.

La Rochefoucauld

The day we were to meet again was beautiful. The sky was clear of clouds, the sun as bright as it can be when the air is a little crisp and very clean. A good Prescott morning, I thought as I looked outside. I had chores to do so I didn't go for a walk. The garden took up part of my time and Sue had me busy on things inside the house until it was time for our early lunch. Everything I did was more or less routine, so I had plenty of time to think.

Once before I had planned a list of questions for Quinn. This time, I wanted to tell him briefly that I was in sync with most of his points of view and then ask the one remaining major question: What do we do about our problem with violence?

Sue and I went to the garage together. She pulled her car out, waved good-bye and left. I got into mine and drove to Quinn and Bobbie's.

They live just west of the downtown area off of Park Avenue, a lovely part of the city. Lots of trees, winding streets, some really charming houses and all pridefully well maintained. Sue and I had wanted to live there, but not one of our trips from Laguna produced a house we liked and could also afford. We bought to the north of downtown, up Willow Creek Road about three miles. We like it fine, but I do prefer where Quinn and Bobbie are. I look at for sale signs, but never go in knowing Sue is settled in and happy.

I parked on the street and walked up to the front door which was open. I touched the bell button and Quinn appeared wearing his light jacket. He said, "It's such a great day, why don't we walk? We can take our time going down to the Square."

I agreed, pleased that he suggested it. We spent the afternoon strolling, sitting now and then, and talking. Arriving at the Courthouse Plaza, we circled the nearly century-old, impressive, granite-blocked edifice that is a comfort and a joy to all Prescottonians, both the newly arrived and the old timer. We were not alone. Others were also taking advantage of the weather. Some ambled along like us, frequently getting in the way of the serious, air-pumping walkers. No one complained. All of us had our own purposes and with courtesy allowed others to satisfy theirs.

At times, we rested on a bench and talked. At some point in the afternoon, we crossed Montezuma Street and sat in the Caffe St. Michael sipping a special blend. Nothing we did, however, interfered with our conversation. We, well actually Quinn, carried on almost nonstop.

What I'm now going to report on for that afternoon has been helped by Quinn's notes. They were scant though. But it doesn't matter that they are less than complete. My memory of that afternoon and the fact that I'm now so deeply inside his head, has me capturing what he had to say without any trouble at all. Most of what I will write will be a comparative action—synergy! I've not used that word before, but read it any number of times. What follows then is a synergism, our working together, notwithstanding that Quinn is gone.

Some of the language, as it has been before, will be mine, but his ideas will be kept intact. Without him, his plan to resolve human malevolence would have never entered my mind. As far as that goes, all of his concepts that led up to our last afternoon together would hardly have ever occupied me. Parts of it, maybe. But not to the extent that I am now engrossed.

As soon as we left the house, I said, "I've given a lot of thought to all that we've talked about. I'm with you so far. I admire human beings for their unique capabilities and their use of those capabilities to overcome obstacles and, to use your term, aspire. I've learned to look at the whole of humanity as never before, and I'm filled with admiration. I see value. I believe we are valuable creatures. I also see clearly the terrible things we do to

97

each other. I understand, better than I ever expected to understand, why we do these terrible things."

"That's good, John."

"I've never given serious thought to any of this before."

He said, "I understand. Few people have. Too busy living their own lives. Too busy dealing with the problems that affect them directly."

As we walked along, I nodded my agreement. "There are several aspects to your position regarding human violence that I'd like to clarify. Okay?"

"Of course."

"First, you believe that a primary motivation in all of us, to put it simply, is to like ourselves."

"That's right. Liking ourselves is vital. The importance of self-regard is well founded. I believe that our great need for self-respect is beyond dispute."

"I suppose, then, that since we are the superior life force here on Earth and it appears in our solar system, we should be <u>expected</u> to value ourselves. Do you agree that valuing ourselves could be an inborn drive? That it could be an uncompromising natural tendency?"

"I do, indeed."

"You take the position that when this inborn drive is in any way thwarted or challenged, we have reasons for most violence, don't you?"

"For most, but not all, yes."

"You have two main sources for antihuman behavior, right?"

He glanced over toward me and said, "One is low self-esteem that can motivate us to attain specific and worthwhile goals and can also motivate us to dominate others, both of which are attempts to build up or rebuild weakened egos. To dominate is to be in charge, to feel superior. That feeling is usually short lived though."

"I see that. Examples of coerced authority are the neighborhood bully and rapist up and through the thief with a gun and the random killer. Then ultimate domination is achieved through a dictator's aggressive will to gain oppressive power over thousands rather than one or a few?"

It was a question. I looked at him and he nodded while checking for cars before crossing a street.

I continued with, "The other is humiliation for the sake of cruel debasement, which can provoke retaliation and a possible necessity for bloody revenge.

He said, "In a nut shell, that is the second source. I believe these two are the principal sources for most violent crimes. But, as I said earlier, most, not all."

"Okay. So starting with this need to feel important, can that justify our defensive, self-protective actions or fiery responses to any kind of oppression? Can we justify the oppressor who is only trying to build up a frustrated ego? How about one group's denial of another group's common rights, which is self-serving? What about the group that feels they've been unfairly denied these rights? Are we supposed to defend their often violent, self-protective reactions? Can we excuse single-minded, hurtful and unreasonable prejudice because it has for some a desirable purpose? One last example: Should we try to justify those people who flagrantly look down upon or treat with open contempt others only to repair their broken egos? Or those who almost by reflex refuse to accept the degradation?

Quinn was careful as he said, "I don't know about justify. These attempts to either dominate or humiliate can be explained. So can the explosive results growing out of a forced control and an imposed mortification be explained. I think it helps to understand why the attempts are made and why all of us live with the responses."

I thought about that for a moment and then said, "Even though I have reasons—even valid ones—this newly acquired understanding doesn't stop me from condemning or demanding punishment for those who commit any of our violent crimes. Should this understanding make me tolerant of some who participate in violent crimes? Should my awareness of the reasons for degrading actions and the instinctive, often brutal reactions, make me more charitable toward those responsible? Should I go so far as to be sympathetic?"

He shook his head. "We have laws. If a law is broken, the lawbreaker must be taken away from society so he or she can do no more harm. Our laws, that benefit us all, must be upheld."

"Even though we know why the act was carried out?"

"Of course."

"So more police, more jails, harsher penalties are the answer?"

"I didn't say that."

"What are you saying?"

"I haven't had a chance." He laughed as he looked at me. "You ask should we be more tolerant of villainous actions because we may know why those actions take place. I say, no. Sadly, we have no choice after the fact. It's before the fact that we must concern ourselves."

"I can't dispute that, Quinn. Let me, however, ask you something else."

"Go ahead."

"If we should punish those who are more or less giving in to an involuntary resentment and turning to violence, what about those who prompt the anger or the rage and goad them into striking back? Don't the demeanors and those who treat others with contempt have to share the blame for the violence? What about punishment for them, even though we can attribute their demeanor to insecurity and their compulsory human answer to an obligatory human need to feel important? We can explain their actions the same as we can explain the actions of those who suffer their abuse."

"We can, and some do. But most want to focus on conduct that is undeniably contrary to our laws."

"It's complex, isn't it? This business of violence?"

"Very. Very complex."

"Do you have a solution that will do away with hate groups, the self-absorbed power seekers and the self-protective, especially the crime-ridden minority gangs? Do you have a plan that will curb those who attack others in order to feel better about themselves?"

"Yes, I have an answer. But since the problem is so complex, the solution is also somewhat complicated." He thought for a few seconds and said, "I'd prefer, rather than complicated, involved. There's a slight difference between the two."

There was another short pause before, "What I propose is not," he searched for a word and came up with, "earth shaking." Looking a little displeased with his choice, he went on, "My proposal isn't especially clever or brilliant. It won't overwhelm or excite most people. With that said, however, my hope is that it'll encourage some people to give it further consideration. That's the best I can hope for." And then he said, quite unnecessarily, "I'm sorry about that."

We walked along, neither of us saying anything until he said, still subdued, "Though we are no longer primitive beings, too many allow a revengeful or a reciprocal violence control their minds. Maybe, after careful deliberation, my approach to solving our tormenting and tortuous actions toward one another will be seen as well-grounded and could, over time, be effective."

He looked over to me and waited for a reply or another question. I had neither, so he went on, "We have a super abundance of reasonable rules meant to govern human conduct. We have had our share of saints and scholars teaching us precisely where the ethical boundaries are. Religious leaders have made obvious the punishments awaiting the sinful. How more dazzling can we make the golden rewards pledged to the virtuous?

"These things work—for some of us. The spiritual-minded, psychologists, students of social behavior, social scientists, some parents, some philosophers, some grade and high school teachers have done marvelously well in establishing a positive view of ourselves.

"There are so many books and clinics that help. No matter how hard we've tried, though, we continue to live with rapes, child and spousal abuses, frauds, arsons, murders, wild shootings, uninhibited corruption and the avid misuse of power."

"Okay, Quinn. Even though it's involved, what's the answer?"

He responded without hesitation; his previous apology now forgotten, "It's a process, a slow one. You've gone through it listening to me. You're not the best example of a person in need of this process. But, now that you've gone through it, you can and have expressed it. You are now able to express it to others who do have a need."

I said, "And that's important?"

"Very. You can be one of those who help others see our inherent value. Help them to understand so they can build the respect that is so essential.

"You know, John, we have countless people who don't steal or wreck someone else's property. There are millions of people who would never abuse another person. Most of them don't know why. They simply abide by an elementary orthodoxy of kinship.

"In our ghettoes, living side-by-side, is a kid with a gun and a teenager who dreams of college. On the same floor of a tenement building, there are kids without a father and youngsters who one day will lead better lives because of hard-working and caring parents. There are hundreds of pressed-down folks in our inner cities who give all of their spare time and energy to those just as deprived. Overall environment is the same, but there are different outlooks, different behaviors.

104

"These are people who believe in themselves—and others. They sense their worth as human beings, but would never use superior to describe themselves. They don't comprehend strong ambition for selfish advancement well enough to discuss it as a common drive.

"They are the confident and respectful and they come in all colors, shapes and sizes. They range from the poorest of us to the richest, from the privileged to the impoverished.

"Some people are truly good and not because of any imagined reward or a fear of retribution. They may not even appreciate that our laws are appropriate and commendable. They're not good because they've found a set of principles, a doctrine or a belief they like. They do no more than live by that which wells up out of a deeply-felt respect for themselves, for their world and life itself."

I said, "Let me understand what you're saying. I don't need your process. Lots of other folks don't need it. But we'd all be better off acknowledging it so we can express it."

"That's right. By extolling the human race, more people will see themselves for what they are. Who best to perpetuate the process than those already respectful of themselves and others?"

"Well, I see that! What exactly is the process though? I'm a little lost."

He glanced at me and said, "The process is

just what had you say, before we were 20 feet from the house, that you admired human beings. I think you said, 'The whole of humanity'."

I responded, "So everything we've talked about has a single goal? That goal is to sell the human being as something worthy of veneration, right?"

"That's right. Worthy of praise, worthy of approval, worthy of our deepest regard. We must learn to be thankful for life, to cherish our unmatched sensibilities, our profound sense of right and wrong."

"And your conclusion is that if we sell ourselves to ourselves as stupendous, utterly remarkable and unique beings, we'll begin to live together without the strife that's plagued us forever?"

He said, "That's what I believe. If, as individuals, we are driven to feel important and fail and therefore fail to respect others, isn't that the basis for our conflicts? We must aim at building respect for ourselves and the rest of humanity. How else do we solve the strife?"

I said, "And those who somehow believe in human value are going to bring about this incredible change?"

"Everything else has been tried. What have we got to lose?"

I said with a smile, "I can't argue with you on that point. Okay, Quinn, how do we go about bringing the process to more people? How are we going to sell ourselves to ourselves and bring about this much needed respect?"

"Hate, paranoia, rage, despotism and over-all lawlessness are limitations we impose on ourselves. The same energy must be brought to a resolution as we've brought to other restrictions that we've decided were intolerable."

"Do you realize what a huge undertaking that is?"

He said gravely, "It is big, isn't it?" He chuckled and then said, "I told you that it was involved."

"Oh, it's involved all right. I'm convinced you're correct about our requirement for overall respect. I can see how some marvelous people through different methods could do a wonderful job of establishing human value in their small groups. But how do you propose we take on whole communities, the nation, the world? A response group is one thing, but thousands of diverse people with diverse problems? That's a big, big order."

It wasn't that he hadn't thought this through, but still he delayed answering me. He took out his handkerchief and wiped his glasses. His cliched delaying tactic did amuse me. I didn't let it show; just waited him out.

With his handkerchief folded neatly and back in his pocket, he said, "The process starts small. People who are in a position to be heard begin the process. It's really in the hands of those who care about our world and the living things that occupy it. They must make sure that reminders of our achievements are made available. Their objective, of course, is to establish pride. Editorials, speeches at group sessions, television programs and motion pictures must extol our authority and the relevance of our freedom to employ that authority. The world's preschools, grade and high schools, and universities must begin to glorify humankind. Every curriculum must contribute to the discovery that our fellow beings are just too admirable to curtail or to dismiss—ever.

"Young people must be taught to see themselves apart from any adverse situation that they might find themselves in. They must learn that their inherent worth is not affected one way or another by events taking place around them.

"We must introduce in all of our learning centers revelations of our astonishing progress. Those who love poetry should remind us that the words used are the sole achievements of the human mind. We must learn to appreciate not just the rise and fall of rhythmic verse, but stand in awe of the vast accumulation of our words. We must learn to appreciate their overwhelming diversity and perfection. All of us must be encouraged to concede that without our mastery of language there would be no poet to embolden our desire for flights of fancy or extravagant thought.

"Everyone must learn to treasure the incremental progress that led to our astonishingly varied attainments. Teenagers must be taught to see that human beings in the aggregate created the mathematics that slowly expanded from one plus one to algebraic combinations and symbolic calculus. They must learn to be grateful for the numbers themselves, like words, and be quick to grant that they did not exist before creatures like themselves created them. The overwhelming feat of measurement should be used to increase their respect for the human family, of which they are a new and welcomed member.

"A new teaching criterion by caring teachers must passionately dramatize human capacities and our incredible triumphs. Writers of children's fiction must do the same so that stimulating books summarizing the unmatched abilities of humankind sit alongside Barbar the Elephant, Cinderella and Mother Goose.

"Human nobility, our praiseworthy daring and our intense resolve to bring about beneficial development must be fully recognized. Once teachers—and parents—illuminate our phenomenal independence and enterprise, our young should know proper respect for their own inherent remarkableness. Every effort must be made so that never again they lose that vital sense of dignity and worth, and the dignity and worth intrinsic to every human being. Only then will they understand that today's hurtful attitudes and calamitous actions are oppressive transgressions against their rightful dominion over themselves and this globe upon which they are privileged to live.

"If effective in a quest for a universal acknowledgment of human significance in the young, then pride and respect for themselves will prohibit—without a search for a right-minded judgment—their harming, in any way, another grand member of their human family. There will no longer be victims suffering pitiless retaliation from prior victims of pitiless assaults. A regard for others must be a free or unmindful choice. It must come in celebration, not as a compulsory act because of some credo, law or rule.

"If we laud, bring acclaim and praise to all men and women, build an indisputable respect for the one-of-a-kind living things with their exclusive, inexhaustible abilities and unrivaled goals, we should have everyone believing they, too, indeed belong in a high or lofty place.

"If we could live together, having given each other unanimous approval, we would all feel as we should: <u>Complete</u>. We would not be compelled to appear imposing or impressive, devote ourselves to accumulating wealth or status for the purpose of trying to be or appear important. We would be forever spared of pomposity and high-flown bombastic words used solely to attract attention. Everyone would be spared from looking out for those who retire from the human race, who care about nothing, who choose to shun attachments of every kind. Corrupt nations would substitute good intentions for unprincipled aggressions.

"There would be no apprehension of differences. Our separate ideologies and regional customs would be looked to for rudiments of sound-thinking that might serve us all.

"With human value paramount, we would be beyond totalitarian leaders for whom no amount of self-serving power has ever been satisfactory. Those self-absorbed authoritarians, for whom no obedience has ever been quite enough, would disappear. We would be released from those who want revenge upon a world which they believe has treated them unfairly or with contempt, and those who want to take revenge in particular on certain individuals or groups. We would be liberated from elitists who wish to render those outside their closed groups irrelevant. No longer would we suffer from debates that are unavailing, that embody no courtesy or a willingness to carefully weigh another's point of view.

"There would be no attempts to defraud, plunder, ravish or shatter another, nor a need to seek the upper hand, to overstrain for leverage or dominance. Simple greed would not be with us.

"All persons would have the right—and the opportunity—to decide on their level of productivity. Each one of us would come to terms with our individual talent and skills or lack of talent and skills. An undetailed, spontaneous ethic would

111

produce the best and fairest government for everyone. We would finally evoke and enjoy the utility of government. Legislators who have a preference for getting rid of the parts of government that serve us all, while keeping the parts that serve only a handful, would be no more.

"People would sleep safely in their beds at night. A cleaner, unscathed world would be ours to enjoy. We would care about little things, have faith in ordinary life. Giving thanks for the trivialities that we now seldom take delight in would become customary. Flowers might then grow where the detritus of the underprivileged and the discouraged now accumulates. Slums, as we know them, would no longer exist to excite our capacity for shame.

"To preserve and enjoy this remarkable planet, we must see to it that no one forgets that it is a marvelously encouraging place of a wide and wild diversity. We must prevent our forgetting that this magical world sustains us in grand style. How much longer can we forge ahead with our being unappreciative of its support and lavish gifts?

"We must make it impressively apparent that this earth offers up to us—void of any obligation—its secrets. We must make plain that it administers to and places at our disposal its entire assembly of experimental effort. That nothing below or above its surface has been withheld from this most awesome living thing, the human being. It must be easily perceived that this world has never presented anything insurmountable, only inviting challenges. Rather than taking for granted that which we see and touch and explore, we should, in our busy lives, give some thought to its unrestrained graciousness."

All of the above was delivered evenly paced, much as I have written it. The words and sentences are not exact, but the essence of what he said is. I thought it a stunning performance. He just opened up and his thoughts poured out. I was overwhelmed. It wasn't the first time, but unknown to me, it was the last.

He had stopped. He didn't resort to the glasses routine, just sat quietly. I remember, we were on a bench at the front of the courthouse. I didn't say a thing.

Finally, he turned to me and said with little emphasis, "With our dazzling imaginations in full gear, human beings must establish a permanent and profound sense of gratitude for life itself and this planet that sustains life. When a majority of us feel respectful of our hospitable giver of wonderful gifts, this lenient planet of ours will never again be plundered or deprived of its right to maintain its delicate balances. We live on such an obliging planet and we take it—and, of course, ourselves—too much for granted. An acquired respect will change that."

We got up and took another turn around

the Square and then headed home. On the way, he brought up the following:

"Should you ask: Is this call to promote ourselves to idealistic or to impractical? Of course you should! But, before making up your mind, you should also ask the obvious: What alternative do we have? And, what is there from our past that might help us solve our expanding emotional and mental, our verbal and physical transgressions? Do we have any plan to solve the profusion of problems that destroy in people any confidence in their being meaningful human purposes? We know full well that the power of art or the wisdoms so deeply rooted in our deities or the stark reality of horrific brutality brought into our living rooms will never teach or shock us into being at our humanly best.

"Everyone has the right to ask: Does virtue, integrity, generosity and our impromptu acts of kindness grow out of a wholly accurate self-evaluation that confirms individual worth? Are viciousness, debasement, fear, hate, greed and uncharitable acts natural consequences of a lack of confidence or faith in ourselves?

"My answer is, generally and basically, yes. And being that uncomplicated means that the solution to what is outrageously damaging to our world and ourselves rests on our decreasing the number of people undergoing the stress of self-doubt or a need for revenge."

I broke in saying, "And adding to those who

114

are in touch with their human significance?"

He nodded, offering agreement, and continued saying, "As you've said, John, there are numerous individuals, clinics, agencies and civic organizations that volunteer programs bringing such values as cooperation and personal esteem to hundreds of potentially volatile persons. They reach thousands, ease their anguish and recover lost abilities. They try, admirably, but fall short of reaching millions—perhaps tens of millions—who need help in recognizing what is of paramount importance: Their own value because they are one of a select, beyond comparison kind of living thing.

"We can also question whether pointing out our significance will turn self-haters into self-healers. Will establishing that our existence is remarkable turn the selfish and greedy into solicitous and generous members of society? The malevolent into the benevolent? The power-mad into the philanthropic?

"My answer is, not immediately in those cases where the pain and a need for revenge is intense and the experience of committing reprehensible assaults is too great a gratifying compensation to lose. Or, when extreme selfishness, intense hostility or an irrational impulse to attain power over others is caused by a biological, pathological or psychiatric disorder. There should be, however, sufficient response to make a difference, and in the long run a great and possibly a world-saving difference."

There was a short silence followed by, "We simply must face up to the fact that in order to abide by our long-standing ethical values, we must first see ourselves worthy of those values. To live in agreement with the truth inherent in "love others as you love yourself,' we must first learn to love ourselves."

He stopped once more, mulling over what he had just said. I think we crossed a street before he continued, "Our moral directives are meant to guide us not only toward suitable actions, but also toward an understanding of the difference between right and wrong. Before accepting their sage advice, however, we must believe that virtue, honor and decency are reflections of the elemental magnificence found only in the human species.

"Why are we blind to an acknowledged human worth being the means through which we hurdle the barricades blocking us from living with little or no hostility? Acknowledged human worth is the key to good will. To harmony. To cooperation."

His attitude changed slightly from being sober to one of moderate excitement.

"Inspired, we can change views, change the world, make believers out of nonbelievers. One hardly needs proof, but just think of the results generated by a son of a king called Buddha or a carpenter called Jesus, or he of humble origins,

Mohammed, who founded and promulgated one of the great religions, Islam.

"Through very successful movements, countless people have attained a longer life expectancy. Women have achieved the recognition they deserve. Minorities have acquired those inalienable rights previously denied. Masses of the downtrodden have been reassured and comforted. Some persons' lungs and hearts are now in better shape.

"To know respect and to love ourselves is our preternatural goal, for the human experience is without parallel! One human life on this planet is more valuable than one diamond would be if it were the only diamond produced over time."

I looked at him wondering where that comparison came from. He was too caught up in what he was saying to notice. He just went on with, "We must utilize our imaginations and create apt, accurate and persuasive communication techniques in order to win the acceptance of our inherent value. These communications must appeal to different tastes as well as various forms of skepticism, frustration and discouragement. Therein lies the involvement. We must be committed to seeing ourselves—and helping others to see themselves—clearly so we can live as we should, in greater accord on a healthy, undamaged planet.

"We must devote as much time to our own discovery as we do to other explorations. We are all participants. We can all further a cause that, I believe, shrinks all others in importance.

"Before we too quickly dismiss that call for positive action, we should give ourselves time to recognize what our realized worth can accomplish. We should consider what self-discovery leading to widespread respect for all of life can do for every one of us.

"Humanity is in need of those who are aware of their significance. They must develop the same enthusiasm found in our animal and political activists, our preservationists and environmentalists. That's the kind of energy needed to galvanize us. We have need of the active participation of men and women in the public eye. And those people with special talents who are secure enough within themselves to speak out in support of human value."

He looked over and even took hold of my arm before saying, "Again, do we have any other alternative but to do our best to see ourselves accurately? No harm will come from this effort and when successful—as it should be—a great many of our problems will be reduced in scope and most of our torments will be greatly relieved. Why should our dreams of human accord be forever deferred?"

A rhetorical question requiring no answer. He continued right on, "For peace, for tolerance, for men and women united in cooperation, for the sake of our already misused planet, for our children, our elderly, our families, for workers and bosses, for the wealthy and the poor, for the talented and not so talented, let us work toward appreciating the true splendor of the human being. We must take on an assignment aimed at carefully and wisely pursuing ways in which persons can recognize their inbred uniqueness. We human beings must be made to believe in our inordinate qualities. We must see ourselves at long last for what we are—utterly remarkable living things graciously supported by an utterly remarkable world."

When we arrived at the walkway to his house, Quinn asked, "Do you want to come in?"

I looked at my watch and replied, "I don't think so. The girls will be home soon and I've a stop to make at True Value. I think I'll just go on."

"Okay, John." He put out his hand and I shook it. Unusual, I thought. We never shake hands. I looked up at his face. It was drawn. He had lost his ruddy, natural color. I attributed the loss of color to his being tired. He had looked this way once before after what was to him an especially meaningful session. I assumed he was just drained of energy after working hard at delivering his conclusions.

I said, "See you later then."

I watched him move toward his porch. He stumbled on the first step and caught himself by grabbing the banister. I called out, "Are you all right?"

He turned and smiled. "My legs are a little

tired from our walk, that's all." He waved, went up the last two steps, took out his keys to open the door and crossed inside. The door closed.

I got into my car and pulled away. That was the last time I'd see or talk to Quinn. He left us two days later to go wherever the Quinns of the world go.

CHAPTER 11

*What reason and endeavor cannot
bring about, often time will.*
Thomas Fuller, M.D.

That's it. That's my full account of an experience that changed me forever.

Quinn's sudden death affected me for weeks. It was too dramatic to have anything to do with day-to-day reality. I really didn't know what to make of it—the strangeness of it! As time passed, things got even stranger. His notes turning up six months later. My taking on the responsibility of recording our conversations. Upon reflection, the conversations themselves. Sometimes I thought none of it happened, there was no Quinn. But without him, none of what I've written would be piled up here on my desk.

When I had finished, or thought I'd finished, I called Bobbie and delivered the pages to her that afternoon. I explained as briefly as I could what they represented. She asked, "Quinn's notes and your talks resulted in you writing this?" She held up the package I'd brought.

I said that I had felt obligated to do something. His view of human beings, our lives and our troubles, was too important to let die with him. I'm sure I didn't say "die," but that's what I meant.

Her reaction was so unexpected that I was moderately shocked. She said, after a long hesitation, "Leave it with me." Her attitude said plainly that she was reluctant to discuss it further.

I had presumed she would be pleased. Possibly even clutch the sheets of paper and say you mean these pages are because of Quinn? You've taken the time to put them in some kind of order? I had thought maybe she'd even shed a tear or two. I left, not knowing how to interpret her response.

A week later she called. I couldn't make any sense of the long delay before getting in touch with me. Really weird, was all I could think. She said, without preamble, "John, I want to bring your manuscript back and talk to you about it."

I tried to sound casual with, "Fine. When would you like to come over?"

"Is this afternoon all right? About 2:00?"

"We'll be here, Bobbie. Look forward to seeing you."

She hung up. I told Sue about the call. We couldn't figure out what was going on.

Bobbie arrived promptly at 2:00. She walked in with a manila envelope, like the one in which she had brought Quinn's notes. I assumed what she had called my "manuscript" was in it. Immediately after saying hello to both of us, she handed me the envelope and said, "We have to talk about this."

Sue said, "Let's go in and sit down. Would you like anything? The coffee is still warm."

"Nothing, thanks. I'll be leaving soon. I have some things to do."

We sat and Bobbie proceeded to make all that happened even more peculiar. Sue and I were dumbfounded as she delivered what was obviously a prepared starting point.

"John, if you're determined to go forward with what you've written, I want some changes made."

I said, "Of course, Bobbie. But I don't know what I'm going to do with it. I don't have any idea of how to go forward, even if I wanted to."

She responded, "If you do, I want you to take out our names, any hint of where we live. I don't want my husband involved. Or me," she added.

I said, "But he is involved. Every page is about him. His ideas. His compassion. His view of us as humans."

"I could have saved you a lot of trouble. Why didn't you tell me you were writing this?" She pointed to the envelope.

"I wanted it to be a surprise. I thought you'd be pleased. And, if I had carried it off, you'd be proud." Truly puzzled, I asked, "Will you tell me why you're upset?"

"I don't believe 'upset' adequately describes

how I feel."

"Sorry."

Sue and I talked later and both of us had had the feeling she was about to cry. She didn't.

After a couple of seconds, she said in a steady voice, "Quinn and I loved each other."

Impulsively, Sue said, "We know that, Bobbie."

As if Sue hadn't spoken, she continued, "I believed we were special. I thought there was nothing I didn't know about this man. You speak of being proud." She looked at me. "I was proud, I was prideful of our relationship, of our years of sharing—everything!" She stressed the "everything!"

"I had small hints of those things you write about. Sometimes in the evening, he'd tell me a little of your afternoon. I had scanned his notes that I brought you. They really didn't make any sense to me. I told you that, John."

"I remember."

"I gave them to you because your name appeared often and I know how well you two got along. I thought they would mean more to you than to me. I never imagined they would produce what I take to be a commercial book."

"I don't think of it as a book, especially a commercial one. I'm not trying to profit off of Quinn or you, Bobbie. All the time I spent writing, I had only one goal and that was to get down Quinn's views in a way that best represented him as a thoughtful man." I added, "Who was also my friend."

She brushed that aside with, "Be that as it may, whatever you decide to do, remove our names. I don't want to be questioned or tracked down by anyone. This has hurt me. Why would he confide in you and not me, his wife, who loved him so much? You may think I'm being silly. It's reasonable to think that I am, but that's how I feel."

"I'm so sorry, Bobbie. I don't know what to say."

"There's nothing more to say. It's possible that what he said and what you've written is important. Right now I can't judge fairly. All I know is that I don't want to talk about any of it. Can you understand that it is too painful?"

"If you say it is, Bobbie, I accept that. I'm puzzled, though."

"I'm sorry you are, John. I've got to go now. I trust you'll abide by my wishes."

That made me a little angry and I said, "Naturally, I will. Why would you think otherwise?"

"I just want to be sure. Don't take offense, John."

She got up to leave. "There's something else. I gave you Quinn's notes. They're yours, if you want them, but I'd like them back. If any of this is to have any meaning to me, it'll be in his handwriting. I may never read them." She stopped. I felt she didn't know how to continue.

Sue said quickly, "I'll get them." She left the room.

I said, "I can see where they'd be more personal than what I've put together, Bobbie. You're welcome to them. Again, I'm so sorry you feel the way you do. I just at the moment don't know what else to say."

Sue came back with the manila envelope they had been in when Bobbie had given them to me. She handed them over saying, "I hope they'll be of some comfort." Now the two of them seemed at the point of tears.

Bobbie said, "Thank you, Sue." She looked at me and said, "Thank you, John."

Two very stunned people walked her to the door.

Before leaving, she turned and said, "I'm selling the house and going back to the Bay Area. Quinn loved Prescott. For a long time, it was here that he wanted to retire. We had years ahead of us, happy years as long as he was happy. He worked hard all of his life. He was entitled to be where he wanted. He's gone and I've got to go back to my friends and what family is left. I will, as soon as the house sells."

We mumbled our regrets. We were too stupefied to act normally or speak coherently. Bobbie didn't appear to notice. She opened the door and walked to her car. There was none of the old bounce in her step.

We saw her only a few times after that. Their house sold quickly. She was busy. Those times we did see her, nothing more was said. She was pleasant enough, but undeniably still hurt.

Sue and I talked about her and Quinn often over the next couple of months. We were sad, but mostly bewildered. True, I had taken away what I considered to be a very small part of their intimacy. Together, we concluded that she had been secure in her marriage, but more dependent than we thought. She always struck us as being self-directing rather than being needful of Quinn's support. She had been sure of Quinn and his love and now there was presumably this tiny bit of doubt. Enough, clearly, to bring about a questioning and a deep ache. That, however, didn't satisfy either of us. We remained perplexed and are to this day. Strange!

We talked a lot about what I'd written. We agreed that his views were important. We decided that they were meaningful enough for me to re-write it. After a lot of agonizing, and with Sue's approval and help, I decided to try.

The changes required more effort than thought. It was easy to change their names to Bobbie and Quinn, names of two of our old and dear friends. The surname of "Andrews" was chosen for no particular reason, other than it was uncomplicated.

Their physical descriptions are off the mark.

They didn't live off of Park Avenue. I put them there, in a house with a porch and three steps up to it.

To appease "Bobbie," I have avoided "Quinn's" background. Suffice it to say, it was unexceptional. We were both Depression kids who made our way without the advantage of a degree, a calling or an expert's specialty.

To simplify, I altered my history—not enough to make any great difference. Details regarding my life, I deemed irrelevant.

The biggest change involved my having us meet because of bridge. The games and their schedule are a convenience. The device justified our getting together so frequently.

I will admit that I'm rather proud of the way I handled the comings and goings of "Bobbie" and Sue, and the various conversations with them. All fictitious, every bit of it. The truth is, I play bridge with Sue at the Adult Center and at Polly's Bridge Center. I delight in the people and enjoy the game.

The man I quote and interpret was a friend. Emerson wrote in his essays that, "The essence of friendship is entireness, a total magnanimity and trust." That describes our relationship. People seldom believe totally in any other person than their spouse. So such a friendship I take to be rare. I cherished it then and I still do.

Bridge had nothing to do with our getting

together. We met at odd intervals. We were retired and had the time to meet whenever we chose. We both took great pleasure in walking. We strolled along and talked more than I've indicated.

Sitting together in one of our homes became a ritual whenever an occasion presented itself. The hours flew by when we were engrossed in a subject or an issue. As I've said, we thoroughly enjoyed each other's company.

He was filled with a concern about how we see ourselves and how we treat one another. At the end, this concern of his dominated our meetings.

He is dead, gone forever, but he lives in my memory and in those notes I returned.

Here in Prescott, his passing went almost unnoticed. A few Arizona acquaintances and a few friends from the Bay Area attended his memorial service. At that service, I was the only one, other than Sue and his wife, who knew of his worldliness, his devotion to humankind and all of the living things on our tiny planet. Only the standard platitudes were uttered. I thought it shameful. To my mind, he deserved and merits recognition.

In what I've put together, I'm able to honor an anonymous man by passing on his ideas, opinions and conclusions. I feel his being unidentified is unjust. But, there it is.

His notes, which I hope are still in that manila envelope, may someday be returned to me to do with as I wish. I would like that. I'll never know if he intended to use them to write a book or paper himself. His lonely widow doesn't know either. She must think about it though, as we do.

We hear from "Bobbie" once in a while. She sends us news of friends and family, but nothing more. She was Sue's friend. Sue misses and worries about her. So do I.

What I've recorded reduces to his view that something beautiful lives and functions inside of us. That this beauty should be more evident, more recognized and more overtly reacted to. That being human is a privilege. That the whole of life is a cause for wonder, which should generate a reverence for every organism, animal, plant—human being.

He deplored our brutality. He wanted the reasons for our vile actions to be acknowledged. He didn't want them justified, but owned up to so the pain of both our villains and victims would someday be eradicated. Any number of times he said, "We are as we believe." Or, "We become what we believe." I am confident human beings are of singular value. And he convinced me that all of us should put faith in and rely on our innate significance. For him, this was our salvation.

It is my hope that as "Quinn" he'll turn more of us into believers—enough to make a difference in this magnificent, but vulnerable, world.